OUTLINE OF SCIENCE

PART II

POCKET LIBRARY OF THE
WORLD'S ESSENTIAL KNOWLEDGE

VOLUME IV

OUTLINE OF SCIENCE

By H. HORTON SHELDON, M.A., Ph.D.

PROFESSOR OF PHYSICS, WASHINGTON SQUARE COLLEGE,
NEW YORK UNIVERSITY

PART II
MAN'S MATERIAL ACHIEVEMENTS

FUNK & WAGNALLS COMPANY
NEW YORK *and* LONDON

CONTENTS

OUTLINE OF SCIENCE—PART II

CONTENTS

OUTLINE
OF SCIENCE
PART II

I

SOMETHING FOR NEARLY NOTHING

Chemical Loafers

ONE of the most amazing developments of the
age, in the field of chemistry, is the rate at which
we are discovering methods of extracting new
chemicals from the earth's surface and finding
uses for them. It is but a few years ago that
helium was unknown on the earth. Evidence of
its presence in the stars was given to us by the
spectroscope, but there was no indication that
there was any of it present here until it was discovered by Sir William Ramsay in 1895. In
1914 there was gathered together on the earth
as much as two liters of helium for experimental
purposes. The cost of these two liters of gas was
at the rate of about $50,000 per cubic foot. To-
day we obtain helium from the natural gas of
oil wells at a cost of about twenty cents per
cubic foot and fill great airships, such as the
Los Angeles, with it. That is but one of the

chemicals, unknown fifty years ago, that modern science has ferreted out and put to work.

Aluminum, the common kitchen-utensil material, was hardly known half a century ago. There was perhaps less than a pound of pure aluminum on the earth. It was more expensive than gold, yet there was no use for it except in the laboratory. Aluminum is present everywhere in the materials of the earth's crust, in the form of aluminum compounds. When a cheap method of separating out the pure aluminum from these compounds was found, there were uses enough for it. There are many uses when it can be made into kitchen pans to sell for ten cents, but few when it costs two or three hundred dollars a pound. Another element put to work!

Chromium was the most useless metal imaginable until methods were found for using it. Its first job was in making a high-resistance alloy for use in electrical heating devices. Your toaster uses such wire. The man who discovered this wire did so under the most discouraging circumstances. The first chunk of chromium he obtained defied working. It broke every tool he attempted to use on it. He had to devise entirely new methods in order to handle it. Now we have it under control. We are able to plate it on other metals. It gives an almost indestructible finish. When plated on gears they are practically resistant to wear. It gives a beautiful mirror-like finish which does not tarnish. Another element has found a job!

But there are many elements which are not yet put to work. Beryllium is usually thought of as rare. Seven years ago it would have cost $5000 a pound to produce. To-day it costs but $50 a pound and could be produced much more cheaply if there were any use for it. It is a plentiful material, altho you have probably never seen any of it. It is about two-thirds as heavy as aluminum, the color of steel, easily polished, and non-tarnishing in air, and when alloyed with other metals makes them hard and non-corrosive. Such a material should find plenty of work of some kind.

Titanium is another metal which is usually considered a rare element, but there is half again as much titanium as carbon on the earth's surface. Yet not more than a millionth as much titanium is produced annually as carbon in the form of coal alone.

Cæsium, columbium, dysprosium, erbium, europium, gadolinium, gallium, germanium, hafnium, holmium, indium, kryton, lanthanium, lutecium, masurium, neodymium, praseodymium, rhenium, rubidium, ruthenium, samarium, scandium, terbium, thallium, thorium, thulium, xenon, yetterbium, and yttrium are all chemical elements which most of us hear of but once in a lifetime outside the chemical laboratory. Yet they all have the same chemical status as iron, gold, lead, and so on; elements with which we are quite familiar. Nor, as has been pointed out, are these elements so rarely heard of because they are necessarily rare. It is because we have found no use for most of them.

Occasionally we find some minor employment for such unusual elements. Argon, once considered rare, is now thrown away in actual tons of gas each day as a by-product of nitrogen-fixation plants. Its only use of importance so far seems to be in gas-filled incandescent lamps. Here, altho used in very small quantities, it is estimated that it saves for us $400,000,000 annually. Its great possibilities are not yet realized even in men's thoughts.

Other rare elements may be working for you to some extent. Thorium, present in minute amounts on the filaments of radio tubes, saves millions of dollars annually. Iridium is another practically unknown material, yet you may have some of it about you. It is used in springs for the fastening of jewelry, in the nibs of fountain pens, and in fastening false teeth. You may also have some cerium in your possession. It is used in the sparkers of cigaret lighters.

But these are only minor jobs. The potentiality of these elements is as yet wholly unknown. At the present time it is estimated that only two-tenths of the ninety-two elements are being used. It will be the chemists' business in the next few years to add to this number. If we are to judge by the important developments which have followed the introduction of new elements into commerce in the past, we may expect to see revolutionary changes in the future. Perhaps the balance of world power may eventually hinge upon the possession of materials which to us to-day are little more than names.

Hydrogen—The World's Smallest Giant

While many atoms have thus been shirking, hydrogen, the lightest of all elements, has been greatly overworked. Most of us could probably name offhand but one single use of hydrogen—for floating balloons or dirigibles in the air. This depends only upon its lightness, for, consisting as it does of but one positive and one negative particle, it is approximately only one-fifteenth as heavy as air.

But floating lighter-than-air craft is an insignificant part of the work which this gas can do, and depends only upon its property of lightness. It can do heavy work as well. Long ago it was found useful in the manufacture of transformer iron. In an atmosphere of hydrogen the iron is prevented from oxidizing, and consequently scaling, when it cools. The hydrogen also burns out much of the carbon in the iron, leaving a more desirable product for transformer purposes.

Now a new and important use has been found for it in welding. Hydrogen is made commercially by separating the hydrogen from the oxygen in water. Passing an electric current through water separates it into these two components. Now, if the two are again combined in a flame, the energy originally required to separate them is given out again, resulting in heat. This has led to oxy-hydrogen welding. Further, it has been found that if the weld is made in the presence of a hydrogen atmosphere a better union results. The material is prevented from oxidizing. One would think that these two jobs were enough for hydrogen to perform in welding, yet still another has been found. If the hydrogen is passed between the terminals of a powerful arc, the molecules will be split up into atoms. If these are brought into the flame, they recombine, giving up intense heat. They have transferred the energy of the arc to the flame. Thus hydrogen performs three jobs in welding alone.

This new method of welding threatens to revolutionize our handling of metals. Formerly large motor and dynamo cases were cast. Now not more than one per cent. of them are cast. They are fabricated by welding. With the modern torch the metals can be made to flow and bend. They can be handled as easily as one would handle cardboard. This method of welding promises to displace the noisy riveting hammer in the construction of our skyscrapers.

In brazing, hydrogen has another function—as a flux. In an atmosphere of hydrogen, melted copper will flow into almost inconceivably small cracks. Thus brazing to-day is usually done in a hydrogen atmosphere. Hydrogen is also the best of our gases for purposes of cooling; for this reason it is often used in the closed cases of heavy-duty motors and generators.

But hydrogen does not give all its energies to the electrical field. It is used in the making of gasoline and benzine from coal. This is called the hydrogenation of coal. It is used in the making of ammonia in the synthetic-fertilizer industry. In this way it is of immense benefit to the farmer. It also has great value in the hydrogenation of cottonseed oil. The atoms of hydrogen are added to each molecule of oil to make the solid lard-substitute so common nowadays.

In addition to all these commercial uses it is this gas which has added most to man's knowledge of the structure of atoms and of the universe. Being the simplest atom in structure, consisting of but two parts, it is the easiest to understand, and conclusions derived from a study of the simple structure can be applied to the more complex atoms afterward. In this way it has been possible to deduce much of our information of the universe around us.

Thus the smallest and lightest of our elements finds the most work to do; and not light work, either. It can, by its heat, cut through fifteen inches of steel, or it can float a child's toy balloon gently upward. It can make a useless oil of value as a food, or it can add to our knowledge of the stars. If our remaining elements were a tenth as useful we should not recognize our world if they were put on the job.

Steel Made with Air

The statement that our entire modern civilization is built upon iron and steel is indeed trite. The fact is so obvious as to need no expression. To say, then, that any addition to our knowledge of steel is of the utmost importance, is likewise unnecessary. It is a subject which is immune from debate.

Our knowledge of iron and steel forms a branch of modern chemistry. To begin with, we know that iron combines very readily with oxygen. It is this process which forms iron rust. Iron rust is, in fact, the material which we dig up out of our iron mines. The first job, then, in the production of iron is to get the oxygen out of the iron and have the pure iron left. This can be done by a method of substitution. When the iron rust is heated in the presence of carbon, the carbon replaces the oxygen in the metal. For many years heating the metal with charcoal was the method used. Now coke is generally employed.

The metal which results from this process is usually saturated with carbon. It holds the maximum amount—about four pounds per hundred pounds of metal. Such material is called pig-iron. It is a convenient raw material with which to start in the manufacture of any other type of iron alloy or steel. It melts and flows readily.

To understand just how this pig-iron is used in the manufacture of all kinds of steels it is first necessary to know just how these are defined. When iron contains no carbon, or a trifling amount, it is called wrought iron. This is the material which the blacksmith is able to pound out on his anvil. It is a relatively soft material and easily worked. Structural steels are those which contain up to .75 per cent. of carbon. Tool steels contain from .75 to 1.25 per cent. carbon. Other steels contain up to 2 per cent. carbon. Cast irons contain from 2 to 4.5 per cent. carbon; pig-irons from 3 to 4.5 per cent., and foundry irons from 2.5 to 4 per cent. carbon.

The foundry irons are made by merely reheating the pig-iron. In this way some of the carbon is removed, and the resulting material is less brittle than the pig-iron. Increasing carbon content always means that the material becomes harder and more brittle. Decreasing carbon content means a softer, more malleable product.

To make steel it is necessary greatly to reduce the carbon content. This was for a long time a process so costly as to be prohibitive. It was the discovery of the so-called Bessemer process, named after the inventor, which brought steels down to the point where they could be made as cheaply as iron. This discovery led to our modern machine age. Without it we would have none of our skyscrapers and vast bridges of today. We should not even have our automobiles as we know them. If made at all, the price would be prohibitive. The process is merely that of burning out the carbon in the iron by passing air into the molten liquid. This, with the carbon, forms a combustible mixture, which actually heats the metal far above its original temperature. Controlling the amount of carbon is then accomplished by merely controlling the amount of air which passes into the molten metal. Thus steel of any character can be made at will at only the cost of pumping in the air. The discovery revolutionized the entire iron and steel industry. Without this process it was necessary to heat the metal over long periods in order to burn the carbon out—a costly procedure.

This single simple discovery has probably affected the mode of our lives more than any other. There is still much room for improvement.

Methods of heat-treating, drawing, rolling, and so on, are being constantly improved. Yet the structural steel of to-day has a tensile strength of only about 80,000 pounds per square inch. Our best piano wire has a tensile strength of over 400,000 pounds per square inch. Theoretically, steel can have a strength of as much as 5,000,000 pounds per square inch. The best we can reach, by expensive methods, is but one-tenth of this. There is surely room for improvement here. There is still an opportunity for a discovery as great as that of Bessemer.

Inoculating Metals

Of late the attention of the metallurgist has been directed toward the study of alloys. When two metals are mixed we do not have, as a result, a metal with the weakest attributes of each. It is not the story of the chain being no stronger than its weakest link. Neither do we combine in one metal the best properties of each. We may, in fact, obtain many different results. We may have a material whose properties are as different from those of either of the metals combined as would be those of a wholly new metal. And this may in turn depend upon just what percentage of each is present. A small variation in the ratios of combination may make a profound difference. This makes the study both interesting and, usually, profitable.

During the present century the steel industry has gained greatly from the introduction of alloys. One of the first of these new steels was vanadium steel. At that time only a small quantity of vanadium had ever been obtained. It was more expensive than gold. It was found, however, that a small quantity added to iron would produce a very hard metal. The metal, unlike high-carbon iron, retained much of its toughness. While the amount necessary was so slight that the term "inoculation" of iron has been used to describe the introduction of the vanadium, nevertheless it was not available in sufficient quantities even for this. Years of exploration over all the world was carried out before it was found in commercial quantities in Peru.

Since that time we have seen all sorts of inoculated irons introduced. It has been said that without these our automobiles would cost at least five times what they now do. We are also told that had the cars of 1910 been built as strongly as those of to-day, their engines would not have been powerful enough to pull them. This is what the introduction of these new alloys, or inoculated steels, has done for us.

We have all noted the recent introduction of so-called stainless steel. This first appeared in cutlery. It was useful in the kitchen, as the knives retained their brightness instead of blackening in the usual way. It was too expensive for use where large quantities were necessary. Now it has been announced that one of our modern automobiles will be built almost entirely of this steel. It has been cheapened, and will be cheapened still more, until it will be used for all exposed steel work. It is a steel that contains a small amount of chromium.

By such methods we have steels resistant against acids, alkalies, salts, and even fatigue. These are inoculated with such materials as chromium, molybdenum, nickel, silicon, manganese, tungsten, etc. We can produce a steel of almost any desired properties now; the future will be concerned largely with cheapening these materials.

The x-ray studies of alloys are now beginning to tell us what happens when two or more metals are thus put together. In pure copper, for example, the atoms are piled together like spherical shot. Each atom touches twelve neighbors. As zinc is added, the atoms of zinc at first distribute themselves at random. As the amount increases, a new pattern will eventually be formed, in which each atom touches but eight neighbors. Next a very profound change takes place. As more zinc is added, the atoms rearrange themselves completely. The unit becomes twenty-seven times as large as before, and there are fifty-two atoms in it. This alloy is very hard and brittle. There is an alloy of copper with tin, and one with aluminum, in which the same sort of change takes place. Studies such as these direct us along intelligent lines in our search for new alloys.

Chromium, the Newcomer

Ranking in importance with the production of new alloys, go the new developments in the plating of one metal upon another. Perhaps the underlying metal has nearly all the properties desired; yet it may not be free from corrosion where it is to be used, or it may not be sufficiently pleasing to the eye. Here is where plating solves the problem.

Of all the more recent developments in plating, that of chromium plating has proved the most valuable. Chromium is a particularly beautiful metal. It has a bright, platinum-like, satiny surface, and is free from corrosion from almost any known cause.

For many years our bright automobile parts were nickel plated. While this added to the beauty of the car when new, the nickel tarnished quickly, and, in the frequent polishings necessary, it sometimes wore off completely, exposing the metal underneath. Here lay the first major use of chromium; chromium plating on automobiles was the form in which it was introduced to the public. And this was but a short time ago.

Such plating is almost indestructible, and its bright surface never tarnishes and never needs polishing.

From this first use we find it branching out in all directions. Apartments are now being built in which all the metal fixtures are chromium-plated. Bathroom fixtures, door handles, and all other fixtures exposed to moisture, when plated with chromium, will retain their luster until the building is demolished. The built-in mirrors in such apartments are also of chromium. They are both beautiful and unbreakable.

And now we find this metal becoming even more aristocratic. It is already possible to buy chromium-plated tableware. This has all the beauty of silver, and never needs polishing. To wash it, it is only necessary to hold it under the hot-water faucet. It will not dry spotted as will silver. This makes the old-fashioned unsanitary dishcloth a thing of the past.

But chromium plate is not satisfied with even this conquest. It is now being sold extensively as jewelry. The beautiful necklace which appears to be of the finest platinum, may, in fact, be but a chromium-plated article. Yet it is beautiful and will neither tarnish itself nor blacken the skin. Jewelry to be beautiful no longer need be expensive.

But there are other developments in the field of plating. It is now possible to plate aluminum on steel in the laboratory. If this can be made a commercially feasible project, we may soon expect to see our bridges made of shining aluminum strands. Aluminum, being much cheaper than chromium, will find many uses where the cost would not justify the use of the brighter metal.

The methods of plating are also applicable to other problems. Nearly all of our pure copper to-day is obtained in this manner. The copper is plated on an electrode by means of the same process used in ordinary plating. In the process the impurities fall to the bottom of the electrolytic tank.

Barium at $12,000,000 an Ounce

Did you know that there was actually in existence and in every-day use a material that is worth $12,000,000 an ounce? There is! This metal is no other than barium, a chemical element easy to obtain in large quantities cheaply. It is worth this enormous sum of money only when it is in the right place—on the filaments of vacuum tubes.

When a tungsten filament is heated it gives off electrons. This is a property which is necessary in vacuum-tube operation. It is the control of the flow of these electrons across the tube which makes the tube of value. Now, any way in which more electrons can be produced makes the tube just so much more useful. Thus the problem is to get a plentiful supply of electrons from the filament at the lowest possible cost. Increasing the temperature of the filament by running more current through it is one way of getting more electrons, but this raises the cost for current and shortens the length of life of the tube. The other way is to coat the filament with barium oxid or some other material such as strontium or cæsium oxid. This, for some little-understood reason, has the ability greatly to increase the flow of electrons from the filament without the necessity of increasing the current through it. In fact, it will, with the same current, increase the electron flow about ten times.

Such coated filaments are in use in telephone repeater tubes and are working every day for telephone subscribers. It is in the saving in these that the value of $12,000,000 per ounce was estimated. Taking the cost of storage-battery power as thirty cents a kilowatt-hour, the power burned by such a tube during its life would cost $13.50. A clean tungsten filament would require ten times this. We may take the saving, then, as about $120 for the life of each tube. It requires but 0.0003 gram of barium for each tube to effect this saving. There is thus a saving of $400,000 per gram of barium used. In the Bell Telephone System alone there are 60,000 of these tubes in use. This means that in the entire system there is slightly more than half an ounce of this material at work; yet it gives an annual saving to the company of $7,000,000. Hence the saving per ounce would be roughly $12,000,000. Thus we find that, while the metal barium is not classed among the rare metals, when put to this use it has an actual value which makes that of platinum, or of diamonds, appear but little more than that of the dust of the street.

In this connection there comes to mind another material which has likewise proved of immense value in the field of telephony. This is the magnetic alloy known as permalloy. It is an alloy of nickel and iron and has properties of magnetism much more desirable than those of pure iron. It is necessary, in long-distance telephoning, to have loading coils in the circuit—for clarity of transmission. These loading coils are wasteful of energy, however. At first they had iron cores, which were later replaced by powdered iron, each grain insulated electrically from every other. This resulted in a great saving. But the coils were still large and, in their electrical properties, wasteful. The new permalloy coils are very much smaller than the old iron cores; they perform the same function, and while their initial cost is much greater than the cost of the iron cores, the saving due to them is enormous.

So much is this so that these coils, resembling doughnuts in shape, have been called million-dollar doughnuts. Again we see the value of getting the right material in the right place.

II

NEW PRODUCTS FROM OLD MATERIALS

Money from Smoke

THOSE who think of coal merely as something to shovel into the furnace to produce heat are now a few years behind the march of progress. We have recently learned that there are a lot of things which can be made from coal. We have come to regard it as a raw product; merely the place from which to start in the manufacture of a number of articles of great commercial value. The fact that it will burn and produce heat is but one of its characteristics, and while this is, of course, important, we have learned that in this case, at least, we can have our cake and eat it too. In other words, we can have as much heat from our pound of coal as we have always had, and yet obtain from it a number of very useful materials besides. Perhaps, as you have watched the smoke curl up from a great stack, it may have occurred to you that something of value might be contained therein. If these have been your thoughts they are correct. In some poor grades of soft coal as much as forty per cent. of the weight of the coal may be in volatile products—products that become gaseous at low temperatures. To have a volatile content of as much as twenty or twenty-five per cent. is quite the usual thing. In such a case, for every hundred pounds of coal shoveled into the furnace twenty-five go up the stack. This does not take into account the black part of the smoke, which is carbon unconsumed because of poor combustion in the furnace—so much added waste. In the smoke which we have been sending out to pollute the air there are materials of value which, by suitable methods, can be recovered.

To recover these products of combustion requires, of course, suitable equipment. It would not be feasible to attempt to do this in every household nor even in every factory. It costs something to collect and purify these materials. In the past, methods of doing this have not been sufficiently economical to afford encouragement. Now new methods of low-temperature distillation have changed all that. It is now possible to drive off these by-products and to have the heat-producing part of the coal—coke—still left in its most desirable state.

In the past the coke which one purchased on the market was a by-product from the gashouse. Distributers of gas for local uses, after driving off all that was of value for their purpose, sold the resulting coke purely as a by-product. Now we are putting the shoe on the other foot. Large plants are springing up all over the country in which the manufacture of coke as a smokeless fuel is the primary purpose. The volatile products are the by-products in this case. The result is a superior grade of coke to that with which we have been familiar.

In Germany this process has resulted, in some cases, in the burning of coal at the mine-mouth, piping the gas to the cities, and sending only the coke by rail. Gas from the Ruhr district now supplies Berlin, about five hundred miles distant, as well as intermediate towns and cities. Here is an advantage over the age-long dream of generating electricity at the mine-mouth, a system which requires a larger quantity of water than is usually available, for condensers. Already in the United States we have a similar project well on its way. A large corporation is supplying much of the northern part of New Jersey with by-product gas from the coke industry. Some of the pipe-lines in this case are seventy-five miles long.

The beehive ovens used in the manufacture of coke for the steel industry are also beginning to be harnessed. The long flames which one used to see flaring out at night from the many coke ovens in the vicinity of Pittsburgh will doubtless soon be things of the past. They are a spectacular but wasteful show.

NEW PRODUCTS FROM OLD MATERIALS

Coal-Burning Motor-Cars

Along with the saving which we are beginning to effect in the recovery of waste products of coal combustion, we are also learning new ways to burn our fuel more economically. One of the newest of these ways is in the form of powder. The coal is first ground to a very fine dust, and by means of blowers is shot into the combustion chamber through nozles which resemble the nozles used in the burning of gas. The long blue flame, which results, also resembles closely the usual type of gas flame.

The advantage of burning coal in this way is at once obvious. In the first place, combustion of coal requires oxygen. Unless this gas comes in contact with each carbon particle, it cannot burn. In the powdered form each carbon speck has ready access to an oxygen supply on all sides, and the resultant combustion is almost perfect. It is also obvious that this method gives accurate control of combustion, so that the temperature of the furnace can be maintained within close limits. The fire can be started and stopped as quickly as would be the case with gas. On the other hand, one should not forget that the use of powdered coal must result in a sufficient saving to offset the original cost, and the cost of operating the pulverizing apparatus and the blowing equipment as well. Again, on the debit side we must not overlook the constant danger of explosion. Dust, in almost any material, constitutes a dangerous hazard. An explosion is, after all, nothing more than rapid combustion, and coal in a powdered form will burn with explosive rapidity.

So far most of the powdered-coal installations have been on land where space was easily available for the powdering machines and blowers. Only recently has any attempt been made to utilize this fuel in other than stationary engines. This is because it has been necessary to powder it as it is used in order to avoid the danger of storage. Recently, however, a few ships have been equipped with powdered-coal installations, and, altho figures are not available to prove the point, it appears that they have been functioning satisfactorily. On ships the saving in the actual operation must be greater than on land in order to compensate for the space taken up by the auxiliary equipment.

Undoubtedly the most novel and interesting use to which powdered coal has been put is in the running of an internal-combustion engine. While it is not generally known, it is a fact that the first Diesel engine was designed to be operated on powdered fuel of this sort; but it proved impractical because the ash got into and injured the bearings. It is now claimed that this difficulty has been overcome. The result may be a great change in the transportation of heavy materials in many places. Even now, in Africa, there are in use many steam wagons which use coal in the solid form as fuel to generate their power. In spite of the fact that it requires two men to operate these trucks, one to drive and one to operate the engine, they are economical because of the high cost of gasoline. Heavy internal-combustion engines which would burn powdered coal would be a great help. If they are sufficiently economical, they are likely to find a ready welcome in such countries as Germany. Most of the European countries are dependent upon Russia for gasoline and oil. Some, like Germany, have immense deposits of coal which they could thus turn to ready use. There would appear to be a real future for such an engine.

Perfume from the Coal Pile

On the other hand, chemists may make such an engine obsolete before it ever becomes a success. Already liquid fuel made from coal is for sale on the streets of Berlin. This synthetic gasoline is the result of the researches of the German chemist, Dr. Friedrich Bergius. The method is one of high temperatures and pressures. The coal is first ground into very small pieces and then mixed with a heavy oil to form a thick paste. This is put into a steel retort in an atmosphere of hydrogen and subjected to a temperature of 800 degrees Fahrenheit and to a pressure of 3000 pounds per square inch. Under these conditions the hydrogen combines with the carbon of the coal to form gaseous, liquid, and solid materials similar to those from oil wells. The products have been described as follows:

A ton of common bituminous coal will yield 300 pounds of gasoline, 400 pounds of heavier oils suitable for Diesel internal-combustion engines, 120 pounds of lubricating oils, and 160 pounds of fuel oils. As a rule about forty gallons of marketable gasoline can be expected from a ton of soft coal. The 120 pounds of lubricating oils are used in impregnating another batch of powdered coal. Among the products of this process is a quantity of carbolic acid or phenol, a familiar antiseptic and also a component of bakelite, used in the radio and phonograph.

In the past one of the difficulties in the way of the utilization of this process has been the cost of generating the hydrogen. Dr. Bergius obtains it from one of the gases, methane, which is a product of the reaction. This gas, when decomposed by steam, yields four times its own volume of hydrogen. Dr. Bergius has estimated that this process could be carried out in the United States at a cost of about $10 a ton.

In addition to these, many other products have been made from coal. We have substitutes for gasoline, petroleum, benzine, paraffin, and so on, and even for such materials as wood alcohol. From the tar contained in the coal we are able to make a great variety of things, including such apparently unrelated articles as explosives, perfumes, dyes, and ingredients of medicines. The list is indeed a long one, and of itself would fill a page of this book. Any text-book of modern chemistry may be expected to contain such a list. Among the most recent items to be added to it are synthetic rubber and compressed gas for the operation of trucks.

It now appears that the coal industry is destined to play a large part in the development of agriculture. For many years our sole supply of nitrate for use in the manufacture of fertilizers came from the natural nitrate beds of Chile. Now, a number of methods have been developed for the synthetic manufacture of these nitrates, and one of the most important of these is the distillation of coal. Nitrates promise to be one of the most important coal by-products of the future.

Bringing the Rainbow to Earth

One of the greatest achievements of the chemist has been in the discovery of methods of making dyes. It is difficult for us to imagine, at this date, the hardships that men underwent in times gone by to bring the dye, indigo, by caravans from the East to the civilization of Europe. It is difficult to imagine the dangers that were later undergone to carry cargoes of indigo around the Cape and up to Europe, a difficult if slightly safer route than that of the caravan. And later added to this trade came cochineal, an American product.

All this trade, romantic tho it may have been, is now a thing of the past. The chemist is able to make more and better dyes than nature ever made. Whereas Nature made but one good dye, indigo, which ranked in value with gold and the precious spices, man can now make dyes of any color cheaply and can even make indigo dye better than can Nature herself.

Something of the difficulty that confronted the chemist in this conquest is shown by the description of the problem which has been given by Dr. R. E. Rose. The problem, as Dr. Rose puts it, was this:

To find how to make compounds that were reasonably accessible, that imparted useful hues to cotton, that could be applied by all the mechanical methods already known to the dyer, that were entirely insoluble in water, soap, and alkalies, that were chemically inert and therefore resistant to the action of light and oxidizing agents and even bleach, and that could be converted into water-soluble products by an easy cheap process, that would be colloidal when dissolved, and would possess colloidal dimensions in "solution" such that the dyes would exhaust or go on to the fiber from the bath, and would return, when on the fiber, to an insoluble material.

It is remarkable that any set of materials could ever fulfil such specifications.

For our dyes we are primarily indebted to three chemists. Perkin, an Englishman, set out to find quinine, but instead discovered the basic colors obtained from coal-tar. From this black, unpromising material have come the basic colors, mauve, safranine, magenta, methyl violet, crystal violet, malachite green, and auramine.

The second of the chemists, who have contributed fundamentally to our store of dyes, was Peter Griess. Experimenting on the action of nitrous acid on such amines as aniline, he uncovered the whole field of the so-called azo dyes. This gave us a whole new series of dyes of unusual properties in the dyeing of cloth.

The crowning touch to our knowledge of dyes was made by the work of René Bohn. He set out definitely to build up molecular structures resembling that of the best dye which Nature had produced, indigo. How could he produce molecules similar to those of indigo? How could he equal if not outdo Nature? His first success was the production of beta-amino anthraquinone fused with potassium hydroxid. This gave a blue which was a better color than indigo and dyed cotton faster than any dye previously known.

Chlorinating gave a greenish-blue color still more desirable. This was the first of the so-called vat colors. As the result of the work of Bohn, and that of others who entered this interesting field of discovery, the vat colors include to-day all colors from the greenest yellows through pinks, blues, greens, and black. The chemist has been able to outdo Nature completely. He has brought the rainbow to earth.

Is Glass a Gift of Nature?

We have become so used to glass that it does not strike us particularly as a blessing. We think of glass as something handed to us by Nature in much the same way as she has supplied us with water and air. This is far from the case. Glass is a man-made product. It is wrested from Nature by the cleverness of chemists. True, those who first produced glass could hardly be called chemists, as we define the word to-day. Nevertheless, they made the glass by methods which certainly must be called applied chemistry, unless, of course, we are to regard the religious ceremonies which accompanied the manufacture in early times as a necessary part of the process.

As a matter of fact, we may even criticize our chemists of to-day and justly accuse them of adding but little to the process given to us by the ancients. The early glass-makers probably did a better job than they themselves supposed.

True, they used laborious methods; they did not have pure materials, nor did they know how to purify them. They did not have high temperatures available, and this marred their success somewhat. Nevertheless, we have learned and are still learning much about the manufacture of glass from the empirical methods which they gave to us.

If we examine into their records we see that they varied from modern practise only in the lack of modern equipment and in the religious ceremonies attendant upon the manufacture. In the British Museum some tablets taken from the Temple of Nabu describe glass-making in Assyria in the seventh century B. C. Let us consider first the translation of these by R. Campbell Thompson, and then later let us consider some comments on these directions by the noted glass-chemist, Mr. F. C. Flint. The translation reads as follows:

THE MAKING OF ASSYRIAN GLASS

Translations of
R. CAMPBELL THOMPSON

A. The preparation of the furnace.

(L. 1). When thou settest out the ground-plan of a furnace for "minerals" thou shalt seek out a favorable day in a fortunate month, and thou shalt set out the ground-plan of the furnace. While they are making the furnace thou shalt watch them and work thyself, in the house of the furnace: Thou shalt bring in embroys (born before their time) . . . another, a stranger, shall not enter, nor shall one that is unclean tread before them: the day when thou puttest down the "mineral" into the furnace thou shalt make a sacrifice before the embroys: thou shalt set a censer of pine incense, thou shalt pour kurunna-bbr. before them . . .

The wood which thou shalt burn underneath the furnace shall be styrax, thick, decorticated billets which have not lain exposed in bundles but have been kept in leather coverings, cut in the month Ab. This wood shall go underneath thy furnace.

B. The making of the frit.

(L. 13). If clear (ibbu) blue glass is for thee to make, thou shalt crush separately:

10 mana of sand (equal to about ten pounds); 15 mana of alkali ash (equal to about fifteen pounds); 1 ⅔ mana of styrax gum (equal to about ¼ pound).

Thou shalt mix them together and put them down in the furnace whereof the floor of the apertures is cold, and settle them evenly between the apertures. Thou shalt keep a good, smokeless fire burning until the "metal" is at white heat: then thou shalt take it down into the furnace which has been let grow cold: then thou shalt keep a good smokeless fire burning until it liquefies: then thou shalt pour it on burnt brick.

Of this and its continuation Mr. Flint says:

In this tablet mention is made of the use of gold, antimony and tin oxid for red glass. These are still used, tho lately in America we have added selenium and uranium to the list. They also mention the use of ferric oxid, arsenic, chalk, saltpeter, alkali (salicornia), copper, manganese, sulphids, mercury and sand.

In other words, in that ancient day they were using nearly as many ingredients as we are to-day. Also, the raw materials were probably impure. That is why they found it necessary to use so much soda ash. Modern batches to-day would call for 1,000 mana of sand and only about 400 mana of soda ash and 200 mana of limestone. Probably the ash introduced considerable sand of its own accord. It must have introduced a little lime also, as they did not use very much.

On the whole, however, the formulas which they used then were remarkably similar to the formulas we use now. What we have learned about glass-making has been limited to refinements in the raw materials, sources of heat, and speed. They used pot furnaces, which are still used in Europe and parts of the United States. The bulk of the glass now is made in large furnaces.

The New Structural Material—Glass

It is clear from this that the fundamentals of glass-making are far from new. True, we have advanced far beyond the early artizans, both in quality of material and in economies of labor. In early civilization, clear glass was a rarity. Glass was used mainly for purposes of decoration. It was accordingly, for the most part, either colored or opaque. We have added tremendously to the uses of glass. Our electric-light bulbs, our radio tubes, our use of glass bottles, glass used as electrical insulation, all add greatly to the demand. One need not think long to bring to mind hundreds of uses which make glass essential to our civilization. Scores of industries owe their being to glass.

Under these conditions it is to be expected that the glass-maker will leave no stone unturned to improve his product. Pure materials go a long way toward this improvement. Consequently he searches the earth from end to end for the exact ingredients which he requires. He wants them in their purest forms. Neither is he satisfied in merely obtaining a result which is desirable. He wants to know exactly how the result was obtained. All this is a job for the chemist.

Glass is about three-fourths sand. It is necessary that the sand be the purest obtainable. In this country the chief sources are in West Virginia and Illinois. We import some from France and Belgium. The sand is washed many times before it is put into the melting pot to remove any impurity. But sand alone could not be melted except under enormously high temperatures. When soda and lime are added, however, a melting point of 2600 degrees Fahrenheit results. This is a white heat.

Such a process would, of course, result in making glass. But it would be glass such as you would not be willing to accept for many of the purposes for which glass is ordinarily used. It would be a dirty green product. It needs many things to make it acceptable. Antimony, or perhaps niter, must be added to give glass the brilliancy which we associate with it. But this still does not give us the finished product. Mixed in with the materials used there is usually some iron. It would be much too costly to remove the small amount of iron present by chemical methods. We must, instead, neutralize its effect. The greenish cast that is the result of this iron is accordingly removed by the introduction of cobalt. The action of the cobalt has been described by Mr. Flint—to whom the author is indebted for much of this information—as resembling the action of bluing on clothes. It requires but one part of cobalt in 400,000 of glass to take out the green color. The addition of selenium also helps in this neutralization process.

The addition of larger quantities of cobalt than are needed to neutralize the green, results in a blue glass, which will become dark blue when one part in 2000 is used. The addition of selenium gives the glass an attractive pink color, which is much used in tableware. Large quantities of selenium give a deep red glass suitable for signals. Copper or chromium added to glass produces a bluish-green material. Uranium makes yellow glass. Cryolite and fluorspar are used in the manufacture of the white or opal glass. The heat-resisting glass, which has come into comparatively recent use, is the result of the introduction of boron into the glass. Only very recently the introduction of other materials, as yet not generally known, has given us glass transparent to the ultra-violet rays, and also non-shatterable glass. Chemists are spending a great deal of time in the improving of these glasses.

In the manufacture of various articles from glass there are but two fundamental processes. Either the hot glass is pressed into molds, much as iron castings are made, or else it is collected into globules on the ends of hollow pipes and blown into shape. Both of these processes were hand jobs until recently. Now glass-working machinery has almost entirely replaced hand labor. One can almost say that only in artistic glassware is hand labor now used. Even in such a comparatively complicated process as that used in the manufacture of radio tubes one finds the work done by machines. Placed on large slowly rotating tables, the tubes pass from one set of flames to another, until each has had sealed into it the internal electrodes, has been properly shaped, has had the air exhausted from inside by powerful vacuum pumps, and has finally been sealed off, complete except for fastening on the base. This is but typical of the modern methods of glass handling. Similar examples could be drawn from almost any process in which glass is made into useful articles.

Such, in brief, have been the methods which have surrounded us with glass, until the idea of living in glass houses is no longer a matter of imagination. In some factories and office buildings, as we all know, the major portion of the exterior shell is glass; but the time may not be far off when the walls themselves will be built of opaque glass blocks. Glass is being developed as a structural material, and such blocks could be manufactured now if the cost were brought low enough to compete with other building materials such as stone, brick, and cement. It is small wonder that we take our abundant glass for granted, almost like water and air. It is well to recall occasionally, however, that even glass windows were once a luxury.

A Chemical Dr. Jekyll and Mr. Hyde

To include alcohol along with such industrial materials as have been described may seem a bit surprising; it does not appear to belong with such admittedly important materials as coal, dyes, and glass. Just because it seems out of place in such company, however, it is all the more interesting to find it here. Industrially it is an exceptionally important material. We see Alcohol on the streets late at night, and conclude that he is a rowdy fellow. We do not see him the next day when he is hard at work turning out useful products which even the most temperate of us will be willing enough to use. It is to this hard-working side of the chemical Dr. Jekyll and Mr. Hyde that your attention is called. Before describing its uses, however, the author is tempted to quote some amusing figures given by Dr. R. E. Rose. He writes:

> The chemist is not much interested, as a member of his profession, in the advantages or disadvantages of the control of alcohol for drinking purposes. It amuses him to think of the Eighteenth Amendment in terms of molecules. Perhaps it would be terrifying to a rabid Prohibitionist to know that a liquor containing one million times one million times one million times 16,000 molecules of alcohol in one teaspoonful would still be entirely legal, so that after all the human body can stand quite a number of alcohol molecules.

Perhaps this is but one of the little jokes of our Mr. Hyde.

But, quite apart from the importance of alcohol in social-welfare problems, it is of great importance industrially. In fact, in one particular it can be said to be next in importance to water. Water owes its chemical importance to its great ability as a solvent. More useful solids can be dissolved in water than in any other liquid. Second to water comes alcohol. It will dissolve many things which can be dissolved by water, and many more besides which water will not dissolve. Herein lies its chief value.

As an outstanding example of the industrial value of alcohol let us consider our modern enduring lacquers. We all know that to-day our automobiles are sprayed with a lacquer that is many times as resistant to weather as was the paint used but a few years ago. Not only is it more durable, but it is a large factor in the reduction of cost of manufacture. Instead of requiring many coats of paint and varnish, a great deal of rubbing down to get a smooth surface, and two or three weeks' drying period, the bodies are sprayed and are ready for use in a matter of hours as compared to days by the old process. This conserves space, saves labor, eliminates storage cost, and frees capital. We must thank alcohol. It can be converted into ethyl acetate and ethyl butyrate, which are used to dissolve the nitrocellulose which is the base of these new lacquers. This is but one of the more striking and recent uses of alcohol in commerce. There are many others, as any chemist can tell you.

Perhaps the analogy with Dr. Jekyll will be even more justifiable if another use of alcohol is cited. Beside alcohol, Dr. Jekyll, be he the best doctor the world affords, must indeed take a very secondary place. But be not alarmed; this praise has nothing to do with alcohol as a beverage. It relates to something quite different. Ether, that anesthetic with which so many of us have become familiar in our experience on the operating table, is made directly from alcohol. If you take two atoms of hydrogen and one of oxygen from two molecules of alcohol, you have left a molecule of ether. With the hydrogen and oxygen which you have removed you could make a molecule of water. Was the praise justified? Has not ether prevented more pain, made more operations possible, saved more lives, than the most noted of the world's physicians?

But we do not as yet know all that alcohol can do for us as a chemical. We have already—in Part I—discussed the use of ethylene gas for ripening fruits and for shortening the period of dormancy of potatoes. This promises important developments in the field of agriculture. Ethylene is another beneficent agent. It is made by pulling a molecule of water from a single molecule of alcohol.

Alcohol is not always a reprobate. It behooves us, then, in curbing his merry-making, to be sure that we at the same time do not prohibit him from doing useful work.

III

MODERN MIRACLES

Heavy Jobs for Bacteria and for Molds

THE enormous amount of research that is being done in the industries to-day has resulted in an entirely new outlook on the part of the business world. No one knows where his business will be to-morrow. One of the last industries to think of research was the cotton industry. Yet almost overnight the cotton industry finds itself in competition with artificial silk. If it had taken the proper course, it should, itself, have been the first in this new field. Now it finds itself in a competition for which it is far from well equipped. While the coal industry was spending most of its energies in internal difficulties, it suddenly awoke to find its place being taken by the oil industry. Now, awakened, it is carrying on research to find new outlets for its raw material. In the meantime it has suffered severely. It felt as safe from competition as does the milk industry to-day. Yet who can say that we may not have synthetic milk?

No industry, to-day, is safe without research. No business is free from competition, and the competition does not stay within a single industry. The customer may choose between a radio, a camera, or a phonograph. He will buy the one which is the farthest along in its development. If the sound produced from the radio is more true to life than the pictures produced by the camera, he will probably buy the radio. Competition now knows no limit.

The fact that no one can tell in which direction research will develop has been a great annoyance to the business man. He feels that something is wrong in a case of this kind. If his chemists set out to make synthetic rubber, he expects them to make synthetic rubber. This they may not do. If they take advantage of lucky breaks they may turn out something quite different. It was in just this way that our modern lacquers came into existence.

To make synthetic rubber cheap, butyl alcohol was necessary. It was found that certain bacteria would ferment starch and produce butyl alcohol and acetone. Acetone was needed to make smokeless powder during the war, and the bacterial method of manufacture was used. Great tanks of the butyl alcohol were stored, as no one had a use for it. Twice as much butyl alcohol as acetone is produced by this method.

After the war great quantities of nitrocellulose, used in making explosives, were available, and butyl acetate was a good solvent for this. Accordingly the butyl alcohol was made into butyl acetate and used to dissolve the nitrocellulose. Thus a new kind of lacquer came into being as the result, initially, of the search for methods of making artificial rubber. The probability is that this lacquer is of more value to the automotive industry than would have been the synthetic rubber which was the original quest. Such things make it impossible to predict where research will lead to. It is the common story of research.

The use of bacteria to assist in chemical reactions is becoming of increasing importance. The same thing can also be said of the use of molds. We normally think of molds as being like that furry substance which spreads over bread left too long in the bread-box; but this is only one member of the great mold family. These molds are often expert chemical technicians. They can perform, quite simply, chemical jobs that would require the erection of great plants extending over acres if we were to do them by purely chemical methods. "Microbiological chemistry is the chemistry of the future," say Dr. Horace T. Herrick and Mr. Orville E. May, of the United States Bureau of Chemistry and Soils, continuing:

Most of nature's growth processes are catalytic, by the action of enzymes. When the chemist or engineer attempts to duplicate them, he takes acres of ground, tons of machinery, the productive labor of hundreds of men, to imitate what nature has done in the stem of a plant or the leaf of the tree, and frequently he makes a bad job of it.

Tartaric acid is formed in the grape from the same materials from which the dextrose also found there is produced, and tartaric acid can also be manufactured from dextrose by a bio-chemical reaction. There is a mold somewhere that will do the same work—the task is to find it and put it to work in the conditions under which it will work most happily. For molds are tem-peramental, but so is the human laborer, and molds have their advantages. They do not sleep on the job, they work twenty-four-hour shifts, there is no strike, no turnover. All they need is infinitesimal quantities of food, a comfortable home in a temperate climate, and protection from their enemies.

Thus we see that there is more ahead for the chemist than one would at first suppose. It is not enough that he find uses for idle elements; it is not enough that he give us constantly new alloys, or that he make merely a better product; in the competition for the customer's money he must strive for an ideal product. But, after all this, he must begin to study bacteria and molds in the hope that he may find one that will do a job, perhaps not even guessed at yet, better than he can do it by purely chemical means. He must put bacteria to work to make lacquer for our cars. He must put molds to work making color-ing matters, sugars, starch, fats, urea, and alcohols. He must put them to work making citric acid from dextrose, as difficult a chemical task as can be found. Such is the occupation of our modern chemist.

Peacetime Dividends from a War Service

Nearly everyone is familiar with the work that was done by the Chemical Warfare Service during the World War. We all know how, by the development of protective gas-masks, they were able to save the troops from the first gas-attacks, and how later they were successful in the preparation of new gases for the offensive. Even the names of the gases used in the war are now fairly well known to all. What have the chemists been doing in the meantime?

Since the war they have been carrying on incessant research. They have been attempting to anticipate everything that a future enemy might do; every new gas which he might introduce. It will not do to wait until the enemy appears with his new gas. We must be able to meet any and all attacks which might come. Thus there are those in the Chemical Warfare Service who are constantly seeking new poisonous gases, and there are those, on the other hand, who are constantly finding ways of protecting against the new devices developed by the offensive section.

Most of the information concerning the real successes of this Service, of course, is not available to the public. If it were, it would soon reach potential enemies, and, in the event of war, all our secrets would be available to them. Some things, however, can be told. For example, the Service has perfected a new type of gas-mask, much lighter than the one used in the last war, which gives greater protection and does not muffle the voice to such an extent as the old. This is a great advantage to those who must give oral commands. It has also been announced that an improved chemical mortar has been developed which will give from two to five times the distribution of warfare chemicals that the old mortar would give. Methods of laying down smoke-screens, other than by these mortars, has likewise been improved. Tanks can now be equipped with smoke-producing guns, and a single airplane can lay down a smoke-screen 8000 feet long while flying at a speed of from 150 to 250 miles per hour.

Perhaps the success of the Chemical Warfare Service can best be measured by its peacetime service outside of its actual field. Many of its discoveries have been of use in every-day life, and these have been turned over to the public. These by-products have been important and numerous, and, realizing that they are only by-products, we may get some idea of what the chemists must be accomplishing on their major problem.

Naturally, their work being largely with poisons and protection against them, their contributions have been in this field. One of these has been the development of a peacetime gasmask for protection against carbon monoxid. This gas is present wherever there has been incomplete combustion. It is one of the things feared by firemen. Being odorless, it is never detected through one's natural senses by the individual exposed to it. He must have some chemical means of detecting its presence. In the past, to enter with any safety a building containing quantities of carbon monoxid, it was necessary to use a mask connected by a long tube to an outside source of air. This was seldom practical. Now a light mask containing a new substance, hopcalite, offers complete protection. It turns the carbon monoxid into carbon dioxid. Hopcalite is used also to detect small quantities of carbon monoxid in the Holland Tunnel between New York and New Jersey. While more than adequate ventilation is provided for this tunnel, through which thousands of automobiles stream hourly, no chances can be taken. Should the amount of carbon dioxid for a moment run to a dangerous amount, a warning is at once given by the chemical.

The Chemical Warfare Service is also making good use of offensive poison knowledge. Being experts in this field, its members have been called upon to assist in finding remedies for all kinds of pests. These include such diverse things as mosquitoes, rats, rattlesnakes, prairie dogs, hair-seals, fleas, bedbugs, moths, bats, and blackbirds. Their most notable contributions have been in the control of the boll-weevil, the marine borer, and barnacles.

For some time the only poison used successfully against the boll-weevil was calcium arsenate. The Chemical Warfare Service has developed two other insecticides which are quite as effective as this material and less costly. The marine borer does much damage to piling along the water-front. Organic compounds of mercury, arsenic, and copper have been found effective in the case of this pest. Test blocks submerged for three years have shown no signs of attack by the marine borer. For protection against the various forms of marine growth, common on the bottoms of ships, the Chemical Warfare Service has developed a paint for ship bottoms which promises success. It is being tested on several ships of the navy.

All ships entering the United States must be fumigated for the purpose of killing rats and fleas, which might bring in dangerous diseases. For this purpose the deadly gas, hydrocyanic acid, has been used. But many human beings have been killed by this fumigant, and it has now been replaced by tear-gas (cyanogen chlorid) mixed with hydrocyanic acid. Long before the mixture becomes dangerous to humans they are warned by the effect of the tear-gas on the eyes.

Such, in brief, is the work of the Chemical Warfare Service in the United States, and there is much the same story connected with the corresponding units in other countries. They are paying peacetime dividends.

Clothes from the Chemists' Test-Tubes

The earliest clothes worn by man were direct products of the hunt. He was clothed in the skin of whatever kind of animal happened across his path—when he was able to kill it. Later he began to use the hair and wool of animals to make his clothing. This was a great improvement. The use of plant products, such as cotton and flax, came as a comparatively recent development. Now comes the chemical age. Our next clothes will come out of the laboratory. Only in the last century have our cotton products exceeded those of wool in quantity. Now we find artificial silk climbing up the scale. Already it has passed natural silk, and the list now stands: cotton, wool, artificial silk, and silk. This shows which way the wind blows. In the end it seems reasonable to suppose that all the cotton itself will be made into artificial silk, because of its greater beauty.

On the other hand, since it requires the best kind of cotton to make lacquers, it may be that this will raise the price of the cotton to a level such that the artificial silk industry will have to look elsewhere for its cellulose. Perhaps it may find it in pulp-wood, but here it will have to compete with the news-print industry. In the end the competition for the natural cellulose molecule may make it economically feasible to build up this molecule synthetically, provided some one can find a way of doing it. It would seem that nature could do this much more cheaply than we can, however, and that we are more likely to find the solution in other ways. Perhaps we might develop a hardy cotton plant which can be grown farther north. Or perhaps we might find a hardy substitute plant. Already a weed which is found in Guiana, and which produces a cotton substitute, has been cultivated in England. This is but the beginning of a long series of plant experiments which may completely revolutionize the clothing industry.

Then, too, the chemist may soon be expected to gain sufficient courage to launch out in search of entirely new clothing products. Up to the present he has confined himself to making substitutes. He has made artificial silk, he has made artificial leather, and so on. There is no reason why new plants or new products should be imitations of anything. It is possible that new plants, with fibers suitable for wholly new kinds of cloth, might be found. It is equally likely that the chemist might produce a wholly new material unlike anything that we have ever seen before, with entirely new and desirable properties.

In the manufacture of dyes we first began by an attempt to imitate Nature. Then we were able completely to outdo her. In the same way in the manufacture of cloth, leather, and so on, now that we have shown we can imitate Nature, let us see if we cannot go far beyond the natural products which we have found it convenient to use in the making of clothing. This we are almost certain to be able to do. We are already entering this new era, and we may confidently look forward to many developments in the next few years. Having reached both the animal and plant stage, and having seen the latter begin to wane, we may now look forward to seeing our clothes come out of the chemist's test-tube.

Beefsteaks from the Air

"If it had not been for the invention—and a great invention it was—of the production of synthetic fertilizers," to quote Sir Alfred Mond, "I do not hesitate to say that the world to-day would be suffering from a famine, the population of the world would have declined, and any future increases of population would have become practically impossible." There, in brief, you have a statement of the importance of the synthetic fertilizer industry which the chemist has created. Let us see how he has gone about it.

For the promotion of plant growth it is absolutely essential that there be nitrogen in the soil. This goes to form the nitrates used by the plant. The plants which are eaten by animals provide, for them, the nitrate which they require. When either the plant or animal dies, the proteins which have been formed through these nitrates decompose and, in part, form ammonia. Through the action of bacterial and of chemical elements, which are present in the soil, this ammonia is again reduced to soluble salts, which are again taken up by the plants; or it may be reduced to nitrogen, which escapes into the air directly. Some nitrogen will occasionally return directly to the soil through the action of a lightning storm. It is this factor in an electric storm which makes it of so much more value to the plant than merely watering with the garden hose. This process by which the nitrogen circulates from one form to another is known as the nitrogen cycle.

It would appear that this circulation would give us nothing to worry about. The nitrogen circulates from the soil to plant or animal and back to the soil again, or from the soil to the air and back again. This would be all right if there were no leaks in the cycle. But such leaks exist. Great quantities of useful nitrates are sometimes washed out of the soil. Sometimes they are deposited in great nitrate beds, as in Chile. But this is not always the case. They are more often washed out to sea, where they cannot be recovered. Another leak in the cycle is evidenced by the great guano beds, which have, however, now been used as a source of fertilizer. At the present moment our great cities, which send their garbage out to sea, represent another serious leak in the nitrogen cycle. True, some of this is returned to the soil in the form of fish-fertilizer, but not enough to balance the loss.

Confronted with this situation it has become necessary for man to tap the air itself as a source of cheap nitrates. The process is known as nitrogen fixation. The first method by which this was carried out was the so-called electric-arc process. This was the method of fixation most closely resembling that of nature—fixation by passing air through a powerful electric arc. Such a process is economical only where power is very cheap. The first plant of this kind was erected at Niagara in 1902. Even here it proved too costly, and the plant was closed in 1904. At the present time but two plants, both in Sweden, use this process.

If we can produce ammonia we shall have no worry about reducing this to fertilizer. Thus all fixation methods concern themselves with the manufacture of ammonia. Now, ammonia is a chemical substance consisting of three parts hydrogen and one part nitrogen. Thus if we can catch three molecules of hydrogen and combine them with one of nitrogen our problem is solved. Processes of fixation, then, are methods of first getting the gases and then combining them.

Hydrogen can be obtained by passing an electric current through water. This breaks the water up into hydrogen and oxygen. Nitrogen can be obtained by liquefying air and allowing the nitrogen to boil off. The nitrogen vaporizes at a lower temperature than does the oxygen. Both in the production of the hydrogen and in that of the nitrogen we have oxygen left. This by-product may be used in oxyacetylene welding and for various other purposes. These methods are, on the whole, expensive and in general are not used unless a ready market exists for the by-product.

Another method of obtaining hydrogen is by passing steam over white-hot fuel-beds. The oxygen is burned out, leaving a mixture of gases which contain about fifty per cent. hydrogen. Tar is precipitated out of this mixture electrically, and the gases are frozen out. This provides many by-products. The needed nitrogen is then produced by burning some of the hydrogen already obtained in air. The oxygen is thus consumed and nitrogen remains. Now the problem is to combine the nitrogen and hydrogen into ammonia.

Up to this point the materials which are to form the ammonia have been pretty roughly handled. They may have been subjected to a temperature of 300 degrees below zero Fahrenheit, they may have been passed through arcs of 50,000 volts. Now we take the right proportions of hydrogen and nitrogen and subject them to presures of 15,000 pounds per square inch, and at the same time we raise the temperature to 1000 degrees and pass them over a catalyst. The catalyst is another chemical which is merely an agent to promote the reaction. It is not itself consumed in the process. It might be called a chemical slave-driver.

This treatment results in the formation of some ammonia. This is drawn off and the gas circulated over the catalyst again. The process goes on continuously, more gas being occasionally introduced. In this way our fertilizer is produced; it feeds our plants, upon these cattle feed, and so in effect we bring to our tables beefsteaks from the air.

How long can this go on without influencing the supply of air above us? One manufacturer says: ''The plant operating at its present capacity of twenty-five tons a day could be supplied with its nitrogen from air over the plant site only for a period of approximately seventy-five years before it would be necessary to call upon the air over neighboring property.'' It should be remembered that this time will be greatly lengthened by the return of much of the nitrogen, put into the soil, back to the air again. Also many of the nitrogen leaks are being gradually stopped up. The scientific treatment of garbage is gradually being developed to a point where it may be expected shortly to restore much of its nitrogen to the soil for use. We may be sure that the time will never come when the fertility of the soil cannot be restored because of a lack of nitrogen. None of it leaves the earth, and so long as this is so it can be recovered. Chemists are con stantly making it easier for us to recover it. So much is this the case that the synthetically-produced nitrogen now controls the price as against the cost of marketing nitrates from the natural nitrate beds of Chile, which for so many years held a monopoly.

This marks a great conquest for the industrial research chemist. He refuses to be defeated by even such a formidable thing as a monopoly of materials. In such a fashion does he defeat even those limitations set by Nature on the saturation-population of this earth of ours. Future historians must look back upon this development as one of the most important of all times. Food is man's prime necessity.

IV

THE CELLULOSE AGE

Clothes Made of Sunlight

WHAT next is to be our great industrial move?
We can unquestionably refer to the age just
past as the steel age. To-day we can point out
among our citizens the giants of the steel industry, the men who have made steel the important
industrial commodity that it is. They still walk
among us. When these men are gone there will
be no more towering figures in steel. There will
be none to replace them as pioneers in this field.
Those to follow will be but tillers in a field already broken.

But we are not a people given to ancestor-
worship. There is still much to be done, if not in
steel. We are now entering the age of cellulose.
Here we may expect to find a new race of giants.
The cellulose molecule is the structural basis of
the plant kingdom. We know very little about
this important molecule. As yet no chemist can
give you its structural formula. Cellulose cannot as yet be built up synthetically. It can be
made only in the industrial laboratory that is
locked up in the tiny cells of plants. It is the
product of sunshine. Without sunshine the plant
can no more make cellulose than can we. The

more we utilize this mysterious material, cellulose, the more we are using this free sunshine which comes to us every day. In that respect we might say that we are entering the sun age.

In the past there have been three major industries dependent upon the cellulose molecule. These have been the lumber industry, the paper industry, and the cotton industry. Up until recently we knew of no other way to use the cellulose molecule on a large scale than through these industries or others which hinged directly upon them. Now we are constantly finding on the market new products which we recognize at once as coming from this source.

Let us consider for a moment some of the more outstanding of these. Artificial silk is a cellulose product. The artificial silk industry is but eight years old in America, and yet the production for 1929 has been estimated as 140,-000,000 pounds for this country alone. Our shops are filled with beautiful, and yet inexpensive, clothes made of this material. The shop-girl of to-day can dress in a fashion that would have been the envy of queens had she appeared so arrayed a century ago. And yet this material is made from the same base as is cotton. It is cotton with the drabness removed. Or it may be made from trees. In this case it has the same origin as paper. Our girls may be said to be dressed in a material not far removed from paper. And yet it is very different from any other wood product.

If we were to follow this beautifully-dressed girl about we should find her enjoying many other cellulose products. Perhaps the artificial ivory handle of her hair-brush, perhaps the little boxes on her dressing-table, are also made from cellulose. If we enquire too closely into the apparently beautiful leather seat on her sport roadster we are almost certain to find that this too is made from cellulose. The lacquer on her car, perhaps in the several shades which make her roadster the envy of all her friends, is also a cellulose product. And as she takes some colored motion-pictures of her favorite football or polo hero the images are recording on a film which has cellulose as its base. The thin transparent paper, cellophane, which wraps the gift-box of candy, glasslike in its transparency, is also the gift of the sun through the cellulose molecule.

We have not come to the end of new cellulose products. Here we have mentioned some of them. There are many more. And there are still more to come, of which as yet we have not even dreamed. Dr. Charles Holmes Herty, past president of the American Chemical Society, has said:

What may we not expect in the utilization of cellulose once we get a clear, accurate picture of just how that molecule is made up? I do not hesitate to say that we have a right to expect an indefinite number of new industries that no chemist dreams of to-day. We are earnestly looking all the time for means of increasing our national wealth. To-day the greatest freely-given wealth is sunlight, the energy of the sun. The question that all rational people are asking themselves is: are we making the wisest use of that great daily source of new riches, which costs us nothing to obtain?

Farming Chemicals

As has already been said, cellulose forms the structural basis of all plant life. It is formed by the synthesis of carbon dioxid, breathed in by the plant, through the action of sunlight. It is present in all plant life, and it should therefore be possible, theoretically, to obtain cellulose from any plant. Any roadside weed might be expected to yield artificial silk. The material thus appears to be very easy to get. But this is a false impression. While it is present in all plant life, it is frequently so bound up with other carbo-hydrates that the process of separation is either as yet unknown or perhaps so expensive that it is not commercially feasible.

In the past the major source of the cellulose, used in the artificial silk industry, alpha cellulose, was cotton. More recently wood pulp has grown in favor, so that now we find much artificial silk on the market derived from this source. In the meantime the chemists are examining every possible source for cheap cellulose. The competition is extremely keen, and developments are so rapid that any manufacturer unwilling to carry on research will soon find himself far behind in the race. Among the many materials which have been investigated and found promising are flax, jute, china grass, hemp, sea grasses, coconut fiber, hop, broom, willow, banana, rice hulls, peanut shells, and even tobacco stems. Some day, therefore, one may puff on a cigaret while clothed in tobacco stems.

Perhaps of all the sources that have been investigated none is more important than the cornstalk. This is not because it promises to outstrip or replace all or any of the sources that have already been established, but rather because it offers the hope of increasing the farmer's income without the addition of new machinery or farm labor. It also may be said for the first time to bring the farmer into the chemical industry as a producer of raw materials. Regardless of how many slogans may be invented for the purpose of urging us to eat more beef, or to eat an apple a day, we can eat only so much. The farmer cannot, by this method, increase the demand for his products beyond our actual needs. He can only make us more discriminating. On the other hand, we seem to be far from the saturation point for new luxuries which the farm might produce in the form of raw chemical materials. Thus the introduction of the farmer into the field of artificial silk, through the medium of cornstalks, may result in an entirely new outlook on his part. We may yet have a purely chemical farm.

Already there is operating in America a large corporation formed for the purpose of making artificial silk from cornstalks. This concern has studied methods of harvesting the stalks and of bringing them to the factory by means which are sufficiently economical to permit them to compete with manufacturers using other sources of raw material. While no definite reports are at hand, it appears that the venture is a success.

By-products of the Farm

Many things besides artificial silk can be made from cornstalks. The cellulose obtained might be put to many other uses such as have already been mentioned—making lacquer, leather, etc. Also we can obtain from the cornstalks certain sugars by treating them chemically. Dry distillation will produce certain gases, acids, tar, and charcoal. The stalks may be fermented to produce alcohol, acetone, and so on. There is an almost unlimited number of things which can be made from this waste material. The only question is whether or not it can be done on a basis to compete with other methods of making the same articles.

The answer to this is perhaps that it can be done where much of the material is available inside a reasonable area. In the eastern part of the United States cornstalks are used for animal food and are therefore valuable. In the West there is grown far more corn than can be used for this purpose. It is grown primarily for the grain. The useful part of the corn plant in these areas constitutes less than half the weight of the plant. The remainder has some value as fertilizer, when plowed under, but it is generally agreed among farm experts that this value is very small. If industry can use the stalks, therefore, it may have them for little more than the cost of harvesting. A price of five dollars an acre for them, as they stand in the field, however, is so much more yield to the farmer than he would normally get, and in addition the clearing away of the stalks means less risk the next year from the corn-borer.

Study of the problem by farm and chemical experts of the United States Bureau of Standards has led to the conclusion that the most promising use of these stalks at present is in the manufacture of wall-board. The stalks are shredded, treated chemically, and finally pressed out into boards. For the purpose of making a complete survey of the feasibility of establishing such an industry the Bureau, in cooperation with the Iowa State College, has established a model factory for making wall-board. It appears at present that this can be manufactured in competition with other wall-boards now on the market. The project is being encouraged for the purpose of farm relief.

It is interesting to note that such a project may contribute to farm relief in another direction. The insulating value of straw against heat-transfer has long been known. Primitive houses and barns were long ago built with loose cornstalks or other similar material piled upon the roof. The board made from cornstalks has also a high insulation value for heat. Because of this, barns and poultry houses lined with such material have greater warmth than unlined buildings, with the result that the animals thrive and yield an increased product. It has been found that the egg production of hens is greatly increased in this way, as is also the production of milk from cows which are warmly housed. The farmer benefits in more than one direction.

The experiments by the Bureau of Standards and Iowa State College have also included the manufacture of paper from cornstalks. The success in this line has been sufficient to induce some men to go into the business, and cornstalk paper is available in the market. Dr. Henry G. Knight, of the Department of Agriculture, has said:

Cornstalk-paper pulp is being produced, and during the last year at least one book and editions of several newspapers and at least two farm papers were printed on paper containing a high percentage of cornstalk pulp. Experiments carried on in the Bureau of Chemistry and Soils and also by Dr. Sweeney at the Iowa State College, Ames, Iowa, have shown conclusively that cornstalk pulp makes satisfactory wall-paper.

Straw, in much the same way as cornstalk, is becoming a commercial product. From this, also, commercial wall-board has been made successfully. Much of what has already been written concerning the increasing importance of the cornstalk applies directly to straw as well.

Thus we see that chemistry is creating an entirely new era for the farmer, to which he is going to be required to adjust himself. Already the introduction of new and improved machinery has made a mechanical engineer of him. Now he must become a chemist as well. With the introduction of powered farm implements the farmer has gradually found himself in the position of a manufacturer. He was forced to adopt production methods to hold his place in the race. Now he finds himself going through much the same stage that the manufacturer found himself in a quarter of a century ago. He finds that he has been throwing valuable products out the back door. In the field of manufacture more than one millionaire has been made by the discovery of a way to utilize an apparently useless, or perhaps even decidedly undesirable, by-product. The same may be true in farming in the next decade.

During this period of adjustment to new conditions, the farmer as we know him, may completely disappear. The utilization of the by-products of industry has had much to do with the disappearance of the small manufacturer. With the small amount of by-product material which he possessed, it was not economical to utilize it. The large manufacturer, besides other economies, had this additional source of profit.

At the same time the farmer may be greatly benefited by this new industry, whose factories will need his labor. Dependent as it will be upon plant crops, it may be expected that initially, at least, the work will be somewhat seasonal, the season following naturally the time of harvesting the crops. Thus the farmer may find a ready market for his time in off-periods. The factories must of necessity be in the midst of a farm section, so that it will not be necessary for the farmer to migrate to a city to get work in them; a procedure which would in general be quite impossible for him, since there are always farm animals which require some care.

Recently the profitable occupation of such off-season time has entered more and more into the farm problem. Not many years ago the farmer's slack period could be used for bringing in the winter's supply of fuel from his woodlands. He is finding it necessary now to buy his fuel. Thus he no longer finds this or similar employment on his own land to pay him during the winter months. At the same time purchasing such materials demands that amount of additional income, which he does not find coming in. Any project, then, which offers employment for this unused time will be of great benefit to the farmer. The manufacture of products, for which he himself supplies the raw material, seems to offer an ideal solution to the problem.

Chemistry and Cotton

There is no more interesting story of the conquests of chemistry in the field of agriculture than that which has so often been told recently concerning chemistry and the cotton industry. While this story has been often repeated, it is nevertheless always new. It is gaining in length each time it is repeated, and not, as in the case of gossip, because each teller draws a bit upon his imagination, but because each time there are new facts to tell. The story, of recent years, has grown like a snowball. It is difficult, now, to imagine that it had such a small beginning. It seems that it must always have been at least of moderate size.

If we go back to early history we find that people were using cotton for the making of clothing. The records are found among various races. But, until recently, no one began to roll the snowball. No one introduced the magic forces of chemistry into this industry. To the Chinese must go the credit for first using any part of the cotton other than that useful in making cloth. Early in the seventh century it appears that they were using the oil of the cotton seed for purposes of illumination and were feeding the remainder of the seed to the cattle. It was fully a century later that this part of the plant gained any commercial significance outside of China. Well into the first quarter of the nineteenth century the cotton seeds were regarded, in America, as a nuisance. They were left outside the cotton mills to rot or were dumped into neighboring streams. This practise was so prevalent that it became a sanitary nuisance, and it was necessary in many places to pass laws regarding the disposal of these seeds. It was unlawful to retain any seeds that were not being kept for planting. Those not so needed were burned by the hundreds of tons.

In the meantime the people were not unmindful of the possible value of the oil in these seeds, and societies for the purpose of encouraging agriculture or invention offered prizes for methods of extracting the oil. In spite of this encouragement the oil was not extracted and the prizes were unclaimed.

Eventually, however, a small amount of oil was pressed out by rather crude methods and used for illumination. Someone discovered that this oil was edible, and then trouble began. Unscrupulous dealers began to use it as an adulterant for olive oil. Others put some of it in lard that was intended for use in the colder climates. On the whole the oil was not a desirable newcomer; neither did it produce for the cotton growers any increase in income that was at all noticeable.

It remained for the chemist to enter this field before any real headway was made. The first of these chemists was John Mercer. His name is well remembered because it is still associated with his invention, a method of making mercerized cotton. While it did not offer any new uses for cotton, it did make the material more attractive to the eye and perhaps increased its sales somewhat. The chief contribution in so far as the industry was concerned, was perhaps to turn the attention of chemists to this new field. Since that time the development has gone forward with an ever-increasing speed.

The first contribution to the art of separating the oil from the seed was the invention of a machine which separated the meat from the hull. This resulted in a great increase in the oil obtained, for that which was previously forced into and absorbed by the hull, was now saved. The resulting seed-cake, made by compressing the seeds from which the oil and hulls had been removed, was likewise more valuable than before; it was relieved from the extra bulk of the hulls. Because of the high nitrogen content, these cakes began to find a use as fertilizer, and because they were now freed from the shreds of the hull and possessed a high protein content, they also became popular as a concentrated cattle-food.

But the process of separation of seed from hull carried large quantities of seed along with the hulls. The fragments of seed became entangled with the remaining cotton shreds which were not removed in the initial ginning process. It became, therefore, economical to remove these by what might be referred to as a second ginning process in what was called a linters machine, these residual short shreds being called "linters." This produced a new product which, while not greatly sought by the open market, nevertheless found a place in the making of battings, mattress fillers, and so on.

Cotton Billiard Balls

It was these four natural products, oil, meats, linters, and hulls, with which the chemist began to work. The cottonseed meal still finds its main use as fertilizer or as animal food, altho it has been found that it can be made sufficiently attractive for human consumption. The oil, however, has had wonders performed on it. Through the use of nickel, to promote the action, it can be treated with hydrogen in such a way as to produce a solid material resembling lard, which has now become so widely used as almost to result in the displacement of lard in modern cooking. Many of our salad and cooking oils come also from this source.

The chemistry of linters is also the chemistry of cellulose, which has already been discussed. Here the changes have been even more magical than in the case of the oil. Some of the products of linters, as given by Mr. C. S. Meloy, of the United States Department of Agriculture, are high explosives, surgical dressings, new skin, artificial leather, sausage casings, roofings and floor coverings, wearing apparel, lacquers, varnishes, photographic films, toilet articles, and billiard balls. Our ancestors would have been astonished at the thought of making billiard balls from cotton.

Now the chemist is attacking the hulls. As yet his answer as to what to do with these is not complete, but he has already made many suggestions. The hulls contain such materials as furfural, acetic acid, alcohol, tar, and other hydro-carbons, as well as potassium and compounds of carbon and sodium. These can now all be obtained from the hulls, but the methods of recovery are not yet economical. This improvement in methods we can be reasonably sure the chemist will make eventually.

To what extent does this help the cotton-grower? Mr. Meloy answers: "The increased use of cotton goods, resulting from enhanced attractiveness and durability due to mercerization, is problematical, but the diverting of 6,305,775 tons of cottonseed in 1927 from the refuse pile into channels of consumption produced approximately $250,000,000 of value that would never have existed but for the intercession of chemical research. It is estimated that possibly two-thirds of this created value reverts to the cotton-grower and thus becomes an offset to the increased cost of production that has occurred during the period in which cottonseed became valuable."

V

OUR MECHANICAL WONDERLAND

Light Waves—the Foundation of Modern Industry

In discussing mechanical accomplishments of man the first thing which naturally comes to one's mind is the remarkable developments which have come through our modern methods of quantity production. One thinks of the Ford car and the dollar watch as the outstanding examples of what can be done by these methods. Few persons have any real idea of what it is that has made these things possible. The answer is, increased accuracy of measurement. Without this our present manufacturing methods would be impossible.

Our first measuring instruments were simple wooden scales. These were eventually replaced by steel scales, which were considered a great advance. Later came the so-called vernier and micrometer measuring devices. These were capable of measurements to a thousandth of an inch, and a good guess could be made to a ten-thou, sandth. Such refined measurements were considered as unnecessary except for very special jobs, and had anyone suggested their use to speed up production he would have been considered crazy. To measure to such accuracy would have been expected to slow up production. Yet this is not the case.

Production in quantity requires that all similar parts of like machines should be interchangeable. A number of similar cars can be completely dissembled, their parts mixed up, and an equal number of similar cars reassembled from the pile. In the same way if a part of my typewriter breaks it is possible to obtain a new part and know that it will fit. I do not have to take the machine to the manufacturer and have him make a part specially to fit this particular machine. In the old days every machine was a different unit. No parts of two machines were interchangeable.

Now, in order that certain parts of two cars may be completely interchangeable it is often necessary that they be exactly of the same size to a ten-thousandth of an inch. It is obvious, then, that the machines which made these parts must be exact to an even closer limit. These machines must likewise be made by other machines, and so on. We are therefore driven back to the point where the micrometer devices, already referred to, are not good enough. In the end we are driven to making our measurements in terms of light waves. These enable us to measure to as small a unit as a five-millionth of an inch.

Light-wave measurements can be made with an instrument known as an interferometer, which functions through its ability to bring together two rays of light in such a manner as to produce darkness. Through the use of this instrument hardened steel gage blocks are polished off to a similar degree of accuracy. These come in sets, the largest being made up of eighty blocks of different sizes. Such a set will enable one to make 300,000 separate measurements. These blocks are as carefully guarded as jewels. If one should happen to fall even a few inches, it could no longer be relied upon until it had been checked against some of its fellows. So carefully are they kept that the average machinist would not see one of them in a lifetime; he would be provided with sub-standards made from the originals. It is upon such gages and such accuracy that our modern production methods depend.

Suppose that we are to make a particular part for a machine two inches long, and that the tolerance is a ten-thousandth of an inch. No part could be produced, regularly, exactly two inches in length. If it could, that would mean that it was correct to a millionth or a billionth of an inch, or as high as you wish to mention. It would be perfect. This we cannot do in practise. Some allowable limit must be set. If this is a ten-thousandth, then the part must be between

2.0001 inches and 1.9999 inches in length. We would set our machine to manufacture within these limits, and we would check the product with what might be called a "go—no go" gage. One part of it would have an opening 2.0001 inches in length. If the part fitted into this it would be short enough. Another opening would be 1.9999 inches in length. If it fitted into this it would be too short. Thus it must enter the long opening but not the short in order to pass inspection. A great variety of gages, usually made especially for each job, serve to control the product.

Another great factor in production manufacture is the use of so-called jigs. Suppose three holes are to be bored in a piece of metal in a certain geometrical relation to each other. No two men will bore these in exactly the same positions. Even an individual will not be able to space these off twice in exactly the same way. But suppose he is given a piece of metal which he can clamp to the piece he intends to bore, and which has holes in it spaced as he wants to bore them. Then it is impossible for him to use his drill in any but the right place. He, or anyone else, will make parts which are interchangeable. In the same way if a single machine is supplied him with three drills held rigidly at the proper distances, and all made to work at once, he is again prevented from boring in any but the correct way. Such gang drills frequently have large numbers of individual drills and will bore a large plate at one time. Large stamping machines are also used to stamp out parts, all of which are alike within close and predetermined limits.

Such, then, is the basis of our modern manufacture. It is a matter almost entirely of our ability to make accurate measurements. Without this ability our modern civilization would be quite different from what it now is. There would be no traffic problem, for example; few of us could afford automobiles. A Ford would cost more than a Rolls-Royce now does.

The Steel Chef's Job

We have already discussed the numerous things that the chemist can do with steel to make it harder and more brittle, or to make it tougher and more ductile, or to give it any one of a number of properties or combinations of properties. But when the chemist has finished his job and has turned over an ingot of iron to us there is still a great deal to do to it before it is ready for use. It must be rolled out, drawn out, or in some manner shaped for the particular job for which it was intended. This mechanical process is just as important as the chemical one, for the ultimate strength is greatly influenced by it.

[83]

Perhaps in the manufacture of structural steel no greater care is taken anywhere than in the manufacture of steel cables for suspension bridges. In one large mill no less than four per cent. of the employees are highly paid specialists who do nothing but test the material. In such a plant the original steel ingots are made up of high-grade scrap-iron mixed with pig-iron. The iron is carefully selected to avoid possible contamination with other metals, then is melted in forty-ton lots and poured out to form thirty ingots. As these ingots are later needed they are heated up over a period of ten hours. They could be heated much more quickly, but this process affects the ultimate strength of the cable which is to be made. The time has been carefully determined from long experience. When hot, the ingots are rolled out into strips four inches square. Fourteen per cent. of the top and two per cent. of the bottom end are cut off and scrapped, as being of inferior material. The remaining portions are then rolled out into bars two inches square, and the outside layer of these is cut off to get down to better metal. The bars are then stored until needed, those from each ingot being segregated. The steel from a single ingot is marked and kept track of through the whole process, so that in the event that any part of it shows inferiority, all the parts made from the ingot can at once be found and examined or scrapped.

In the next process these bars are again slowly heated and rolled out into rods. These are tested for size and strength. A long heat treatment follows, after which the material goes through a bath of fine carbonaceous matter and from there directly into a lead bath. Pickling in a bath of fine hydrochloric acid follows this and quickly shows up any surface defects which would otherwise go undetected. The bars are then rinsed to remove most of the acid and run through limewater to neutralize what may remain. A long heating process removes any hydrogen which may have gotten into the metal through the pickling process. At this stage the rods are cold-drawn into wires, which are then galvanized to prevent rust.

This ends the process except for testing. The wire is tested for strength, elasticity, elastic limit, bending, thickness of galvanized coating, and a dozen other things. They are made up into cables and these are again tested. One large tensile-strength machine in the United States will exert pulls of a million and a half pounds. Both ends of every coil of wire that goes into such cables are tested separately for a great many properties.

When the cables are shown to meet specifications in every way they are ready to go into the structure of a suspension bridge, which, after all, is nothing but a roadway hung upon wires. Even then, in spite of all the tests, we cannot be sure that all will be well. If the entire process has not been carried out with the greatest care the wires may change their structure and weaken after being put into place, and no longer be capable of sustaining the loads at which they were tested before being used. Only recently it was found necessary to stop work on a 1200-foot span because it was found that in a half-strand of cable 130 out of the 180 wires were broken. This occurred before the roadway was entirely in place. The wires had been made by a process other than the one just described. To rectify the defect in that cable will, of course, involve an enormous expense, now that the cables have all been spun and placed. The job of the bridge-chef in the steel kitchen is an important one, even tho the chemist may have provided him with the raw material.

Flowing Metals Together

Our first construction material was wood, and methods of handling wood have been handed along with those of other materials as they came into use. This has been the case with metals. Wooden beams had to be bolted together; you cannot melt wood and make it flow. Thus, when we began to use metal we bolted it too, altho it can be melted and made to flow together into a single strong piece of metal. The result has been that only recently has suitable welding apparatus been devised to allow us to use metals as metals and not as wood. Now welding appears to be coming into its own.

Welding has many obvious advantages. It forms a more rigid whole than is usually obtained by bolting, as the structure is a unit and not a number of pieces held together by angle-irons at the joints. The material is not weakened by bolt-holes, nor is careful alinement of parts, to bring bolt-holes together, necessary. Welding also has the advantage of quietness. The noisy riveting hammer has no place in welding. Also—and this is of great importance—in welded buildings and bridges it has been found that a saving of about forty per cent. in material can be effected. The saving is due partly to the increased strength—as the result of elimination of rivet-holes—and partly to the elimination of gusset-plates.

Welding has gained a far greater headway in manufacture than in building construction. Not more than one per cent. of dynamo and motor cases are cast now, whereas a few years ago they were all cast. They are now fabricated from standard steel parts. The same is becoming true in motor-car manufacture. In one low-priced car manufactured in quantity the only casting is in the engine. All other parts are welded together.

There are several methods of welding. The most common, at present, is gas welding. Nearly everyone has seen it used in the local garage. It consists of burning oxygen and acetylene together in a welding-torch. Under such a flame the metal quickly becomes molten and the joint is built up with a metal welding rod, which the operator feeds in with his hand. Ship propellers, as much as three feet in diameter, are welded in this way. The flame can be used under water, the pressure of the gas keeping the flame from being extinguished.

Electric welding is done by connecting one end of the material to be welded to one side of a low-voltage transformer with large energy output. The other end is attached to a welding wire. As this is touched to the metal and then withdrawn, an arc, having intense heat, is formed. The heat of the arc melts the metal, and the parts flow together. Another type of electric welding is resistance welding. Two parts to be joined are connected to the two ends respectively of the electrical output. These are then touched together and quickly withdrawn a short distance. The arc which follows fuses the metals. They are then quickly brought together again, and at the same time the current is shut off. The fused metals are forced together under pressure and a good joint results. This method is much used in automobile manufacture.

Another type of electric welding, somewhat similar to resistance welding, is spot welding. In this case there are arranged two permanent electrodes which can be brought very close together. Two pieces of metal to be joined are brought together between these electrodes so that the spot to be welded rests on one of them. The other electrode is brought down to touch the opposite side of the metal and a hot arc is formed. In sheet metal a spot about half an inch in diameter is fused together. The electrode is then quickly withdrawn and the metal allowed to cool. This method is much used in the construction of steel automobile bodies.

Such construction has brought into being a great many welding engineers in both the designing and construction fields. It requires an entirely different outlook and a new technique to handle metals in this way. Entirely new possibilities have been opened up with the introduction of welding into the engineering courses.

When It Pays to Junk Good Machines

In the present age we have been frequently accused of throwing away things which are perfectly good and might have been used for many more years. This apparent wastefulness seems to be associated with America. We are accused of tearing down our buildings almost before they are completed. It is a surprize to a visitor in America to see perfectly good buildings, capable of years of service, being dismantled. He is likewise surprized at times to see some of our automobiles that are being sent to the junk-heap. This appears to be a form of American extravagance. As a matter of fact, it is probably one of the greatest, if not the greatest, factor in our prosperity. Suppose we were to find in a storehouse a car which cost two-thousand dollars ten years ago. Suppose that every part of it was as good as when it was placed there, and that it had never been used. How much would you give for it? Certainly not much. By improved methods of manufacture a thousand-dollar car to-day is as good as that old one in so far as the workmanship is concerned. But your car to-day will be lacquered and not painted. The finish will be much more enduring. It will have chromium plating instead of nickel. It will have four-wheel brakes, the engine will be more powerful, it will be built of better steel, the tires will last three times as long, and so on. You could not give the old car away. Our idea of what a car should look like also has changed. The old car would be uneconomical to run.

In the meantime the factory equipment, too, has changed. A manufacturer who tried to make the modern car with the old equipment would find himself paying more to make the car than he could sell it for.

Let us consider another type of obsolescence. Let us assume that a machine has been designed to turn out a particular product and that the machine is perfect. Now let us increase our production until we have two, ten, and eventually twenty, of these machines at work. While each machine is perfect in itself, it has become, nevertheless, obsolete for our purpose. Why? In the first place we are using up too much floor space. Floor space varies as the square of the dimension, while volume varies as the cube. Using larger machines would give the same capacity with a reduction in floor space used. With floor space goes cost of heat, light, ventilation, and so on. In addition a few large machines will mean fewer attendants. Thus wages and floor space are saved. It has been estimated in one case that the replacement of twenty small units by four large ones resulted in a saving of four-fifths of the floor space. There is also a saving in cost of inspection, lubrication, adjustment, cleaning, and in power, through the use of fewer but larger motors.

In special cases, where the process requires heat, there is also a saving here. The surface from which heat can be radiated goes up with the square of the dimension, while the volume goes up as the cube. Where dust or fumes must be removed there is a saving in the number of flues which must be installed.

But the big machine may not be the same as the small one. We may be able to use motor instead of man power. We may be able to install automatic control. We may be able to substitute a continuous process for a batch process, and so on. All these make for great savings and more uniform product. Thus a perfect machine may become obsolete because it is too small for the output. Too many units are required.

Again obsolescence may be brought about overnight by a new invention, or by a change in style. Obsolescence is something which cannot be written off at so much per year as in the case of the ordinary depreciation. It comes upon us more like a fire in most cases. But in the end it is the recognition of the existence of obsolescence which goes to make a great manufacturing nation.

Mechanical Donkeys for Logging

Logging, like almost every other industry, has adopted the methods of large-scale operation. One normally thinks of a logging camp as being mainly a winter affair dependent upon the snow for making the hauling of logs easier. As a matter of fact, logging is now an all-year occupation, and the winter, because of its snow, is the least favorable season. All logging is now done by power machinery. In a strictly modern camp one will not see a single horse or mule. It is because of this change that the snow now offers an obstruction rather than an advantage.

In modern logging the first necessity is to construct a railroad right to the point where the logs are to be harvested. This is often a difficult and expensive thing to do, for the country is almost always rough and rocky. It is usually necessary to span a few gullies with trestle-work. All this takes time and a great deal of capital.

In harvesting a particular region a particularly tall straight tree is first chosen, which becomes known as the spar-tree. It will be the central point of all operations in that region, and the railroad will be built up to where it stands. This tree is stripped of its branches and the whip-like top is blown off with dynamite. It is then carefully guyed by steel cables stretching in all directions to other trees or stumps. In the logging districts on the west coast such a tree may be frequently as much as ten feet in diameter. When thoroughly guyed it has the appearance of the framework of a great circus tent.

From this tree cables will be run out to a second tree, called a tail-tree. This, depending upon the contour of the land, may be 1000 to 5000 feet from the spar-tree. An overhead cable carrying what is known as a bicycle—a pair of wheels which run along it—is an important connection between these two trees. This cable is used to draw in the immense logs. A large pair of tongs grapple the log, which is raised into the air and carried overhead to the spar-tree. As such logs gain speed, and go sailing through the air, they frequently strike trees as much as a foot or more in diameter and knock them down by sheer momentum. If the contour of the land does not permit the use of a wholly overhead system, one end of the log will be raised and the other allowed to drag. The deep gullies that are cut into the ground by the tree-ends are astonishing.

When the logs are collected at the spar-tree they are loaded upon railroad trucks, which are held together by the logs themselves. The ends of the logs rest upon a row of spikes which top the truck. This avoids the necessity of bringing sawing equipment into the woods to saw them all into equal car-lengths.

When the logs are taken to the nearest waterway they are made up into great rafts held together by a crib. Such rafts are often as much as a thousand feet long and may extend to as much as thirty feet below the surface of the water. Often they are towed to a destination a thousand miles or more from where the trees grew.

Thus we see that the donkey driver, with his long snake whip, has disappeared from the woods. In his place we have now a skilled engineer. The blacksmith's cabin has been replaced by the machine shop. These shops are often so complete that they do all their own foundry work. They cast their own brake-shoes for the trains; their lathes can turn down a locomotive wheel. Thus has logging, like everything else, given way to large-scale operation by power machinery. You are as likely to see a horse-drawn vehicle in a logging camp as to see one used in an automobile factory to transport parts from one department to another. The mechanical engineer has invaded the woods.

Have We Become Tunnel-Minded?

In spite of the fact that the world has become air-minded of late, there are apparently a number of individuals who have become quite the reverse, tunnel-minded. They are digging deeper and deeper into the earth and building longer and longer tunnels. One of the most interesting of these is the Holland Tunnel, which connects New York and New Jersey. This is of particular interest because it is the first great vehicular tunnel. The entire problem was greatly complicated by the necessity of providing certain protection against poisonous exhaust gases from the motors of the cars passing through. The principal contribution to tunnel-building which has been made by the Holland Tunnel was the solution of this problem. It has been so well solved that it can be said that the air in this tunnel is purer than that found in our city streets where similar traffic conditions exist. This is all taken care of automatically in such a way as to be almost certain of no possible failure, yet additional safeguards are set up in automatic signals which will give ample warning should there be any approach toward danger. The air is constantly analyzed.

The building of this tunnel has stimulated the building of similar tunnels elsewhere. A tunnel is being built under the river at Detroit to connect with Canada. A tunnel is being built connecting Oakland, California, with Alameda. This latter is of interest mainly because it is not a true tunnel at all, but a series of segments, from two hundred to three hundred feet long, each precast in steel and cement, sunk in place and joined end to end.

The Moffat Tunnel through the Rockies, which was recently built, held the title of America's longest for only a few months. It was superseded early in 1929 by the tunnel through the Cascades, about 100 miles east of Seattle. This tunnel is exceeded in length by but four others —the Simplon, St. Gothard, Loetschberg, and Mont Cenis tunnels in the Alps. It is about eight miles in length.

This tunnel is of interest because of the

method of construction. In order to build it in the record time of three years it was necessary to have as many working surfaces as possible. To accomplish this a pioneer tunnel, a bit to one side of the main tunnel, was constructed and kept ahead of the main tunnel. The pioneer bore was eight feet by nine in cross-section. It tapped into the main tunnel at about every fifteen hundred feet. Through this the supply trains brought in the supplies, and through it the rock was removed. It also contained all the cables which were necessary for the work. In this way the main tunnel was cleared of all obstruction and additional working faces were made available. As soon as a section was built, the cement lining could immediately be put in place, the workers being absolutely unhampered by what was going on further in the tunnel. This method of construction was found to be entirely successful and will doubtless be repeated in future borings.

At the present time the impetus which has recently been given to tunnel building has resulted in a reconsideration of such long-talked-of projects as the Dover-Calais Tunnel. Active steps are being taken to bring this into being. The building of a tunnel from Gibraltar to Africa seems also a not-too-impossible thought to entertain. It is estimated that such a tunnel would cost $1,930,000,000. While this seems a large sum, when one considers the effect it would doubtless have upon northern Africa it would appear that the benefits it would be likely to confer would wholly justify the enormous expense.

VI

MAN DEFIES THE ELEMENTS

Push-Button Weather

PRIMITIVE man was wholly at the mercy of the elements. Not until he built his first shelter did he attempt in any way to shield himself from the weather. And it was long after this that he built his first meager fire to protect him from the winter's cold. At this stage matters stood almost to the present time. While great discoveries in science were made, while astronomy, and chemistry, and mathematics flourished, very little was done for human comfort. Man advanced little from the primitive type of open fire, except merely that he learned to avoid some of its smokiness. It was Benjamin Franklin who invented the first stove—the first advance in centuries. With the invention of the stove came house-heating for the first time. Yet those who have lived in a stove-heated house know that it was the modern furnace which really gave us warmth in winter.

Now we are ready to do something about the summer's heat. At present our homes are at best equipped with but a few electric fans, which produce not more than a ripple. They are about as effective against the summer heat as was our ancestors' open fire against the cold. They are only a beginning in the direction of all-year comfort.

The theaters have been leaders in this direction. When one steps into a modern theater on a hot summer's night he now expects to find ideal weather inside. Many patrons admit attending the summer theater for just this reason. Some of our large department stores are following this lead, and shoppers are showing their approval. Ideal weather can now be manufactured at will. It is common in our large public gathering places; it will soon be common in our homes.

How is ideal weather made? In the theaters in New York the patrons must be furnished with thirty cubic feet of air per minute, of which twenty-five per cent. must be brought in from outside. The air which is brought in is first cleaned of all dust and smoke by washing it out with a water spray. The air is then passed through a chamber which is maintained, by artificial refrigeration, at a temperature of about 42 degrees Fahrenheit. If the air is colder than that as it comes from outside, this process will add moisture, for the amount of moisture air can hold depends upon the temperature. If the air is hotter, it will, in general, lose moisture, unless the humidity at the higher temperature happens to be low already for other reasons. Thus, as the air passes from this chamber, it will in the end always have the same amount of moisture; that amount which the air at 42 degrees can hold at saturation. The next process consists in merely heating the air up to 70 degrees Fahrenheit, after which it is passed out into the theater. At this point the humidity will be about sixty per cent. Part of this air is later drawn out and recirculated with the air coming in from outside. The temperature and humidity just named are considered ideal for humans.

Manufactured weather is now figuring largely in our research. As a result laboratories with push-button weather are becoming common. At Johns Hopkins University zero weather and fogs can be produced at will for the purpose of studying common colds. The Bureau of Mines is studying the behavior of airplanes in manufactured weather. As airplanes must go from hot to cold altitudes and from high to low pressures in a very short time, these studies are valuable. Here the airplane can be kept stationary in all kinds of complicated tests, and the weather can be varied in a manner which would only rarely happen in practise, and which might cost many lives if it did. All kinds of extremes can be tried out at leisure.

Manufacturers of cameras also maintain extensive research laboratories for the study of weather effects on their products. Both the cameras and films, as well as developers and other chemical products, are taken to all parts of the world. Their cameras may find use in the arctic snows or in the tropical jungles. At the throw of a switch the weather conditions of these places may be produced in the factories.

Museums and libraries are rapidly installing artificial weather. The effect of dryness on bookbindings is all too well known. Also the effect on the paper is great. With proper conditions of humidity and the constant circulation of fresh warm air through the stacks, the books almost never disintegrate. Fresh air for books seems almost as important as fresh air for humans. In museums the paintings are greatly damaged by the abrasive action of dust. The removal of dust also saves a great deal of labor in cleaning— cleaning which is frequently damaging to the article cleaned. The addition of water to the air also prevents rare old pieces from falling apart. It keeps them in a fresh state.

There can, of course, be no question but that ideal weather is a health factor. It has been found to have an effect upon blood pressure, respiration, pulse rate, and body temperature. All these directly affect the health. Wherever humans are required to work in polluted atmospheres, provision is now being made to supply plenty of fresh air. A few years ago there was not an adequately ventilated chemical laboratory in the country. The new ones are all providing for artificial weather.

At present our air-conditioning systems are efficient in the case of large buildings requiring large amounts of air. For our homes they are not yet built in a manner which makes them feasible to operate. This, however, we may confidently expect will soon be accomplished, and we may look forward to seeing our residences supplied a few years hence with air that will be the same all the year round. We shall have completely conquered the weather.

Air Sewage

Much of the necessity of air-conditioning has been brought upon us by the cloud of smoke which is poured out into the atmosphere by the numerous heating plants of the city. We are beginning to learn something of the necessity of purifying our air, just as we have learned the necessity of purifying our water supply. If the water comes to us polluted, we must purify it ourselves before use. The same thing applies to the sewage of the air, which is now being discharged, in most cities, almost without hindrance.

Most cities have some law which prohibits dense black smoke. This takes care of only part of the discharge, however; and while the densest smoke does the most damage in smudging buildings, draperies, etc., there are other unseen components of smoke which are fully as undesirable. About ten per cent. of the weight of the coal comes out of the stack, and of this about two-tenths is unconsumed carbon. It is desirable to save this, as it is the part of the coal which produces the heat; and, in the case of large installations, an attempt is made to save as much of it as possible. It is not economical to save it all, however. The remaining eight-tenths of that which comes out of the stack is mainly ash, which, apart from the dust which it creates on the street and in our homes, is more or less harmless.

Along with these solid products come gases; for example, carbon monoxid, a poisonous gas which, however, is soon converted to carbon dioxid and so gives no trouble; or sulfur dioxid, a really harmful gas. This latter combines with water vapor to form sulfuric acid. This is very active, and in some parts of New York is so plentiful in the air that it has eaten away metal cornices of buildings and has made it necessary to close up metal ventilating systems because of holes eaten in the metal. It is destructive to everything it touches. Its action on fine draperies and other delicate materials is all too evident. The damage this acid may be expected to do in a museum of art needs no comment.

In addition to the damage which is done directly by smoke pollution there is another vital factor. The smoke screen cuts off the ultra-violet radiation from the sun during the greater part of the year. That this is a vital factor of health, and particularly in the bone-growth of children, there is no longer any doubt. It has been proved over and over again. This factor can be replaced to some extent by treatment with vitamin-bearing foods and by irradiation with artificial sunlight. Too often, however, this is not done. It requires, at times, much effort on the part of the individual, and often the expense of such treatment is beyond the reach of those who need it most. Here is something given to us by nature, of which we have been robbed.

But how to get rid of the smoke screen, that is the question. At the present time there are many types of smoke collectors intended for the stacks of large power installations. The smoke is caught by these in various ways. In the simplest type, the smoke is merely trapped by filtering it through some material such as metal wool. It may be caught by passing it through baffles or through zones of still air.

The more elaborate smoke collectors precipitate the solid matter by fortuitous air currents. One of these, by a rotary device, throws the smoke and dust to the outside of the machine where it is collected in much the same way that milk and cream are separated. Another employs the principle of the whirlwind. When the air is set into rotation, solid particles tend to settle in the center of the vortex as leaves collect in the center of a small whirlwind on a gusty day in autumn. Still another smoke collector operates electrically. The smoke circulates between large plates which are electrically charged to a high potential. The smoke particles, becoming charged by induction, are pulled over and precipitated on the plates, from which they later fall.

By such devices large quantities of smoke are collected. One single power plant collects over a hundred tons of smoke a day. But there is little incentive to do this. The smoke is no use after it is collected. It will not pack solid, so it cannot be used to fill in waste land. It will blow off open trucks, and so can only be transported with difficulty. It cannot be dumped into a stream, as it will not settle to the bottom. It pollutes the water. Thus there is no likelihood that anyone will go to the trouble and expense of collecting such material unless forced by public opinion. This, however, is being aroused. Unfortunately, no collecting device exists which can be used on small installations. Perhaps one will be devised when the public is sufficiently interested. In the meantime we can look for a major improvement only in the use of better coal and in improved firing methods. This is a problem for engineers and scientists. Perhaps it will mean that eventually our heat and power will come into the cities through outside electric and gas plants.

Permanent Peace with the Mississippi

Against no force of nature is man more helpless than against the flood, once it is upon him. The water rises, relentlessly, inch by inch, until it becomes a great torrent carrying everything before it. The story has been so often repeated that it is a familiar one to all. We have heard of it recently in the Mississippi Valley. We have heard of it in Vermont.

But in the case of the Mississippi, at least, we are preparing to end these disasters. An appropriation of $325,000,000 has been made to provide engineering works for the permanent protection of 20,000,000 acres of the world's most fertile land. When this work is ended it will form an enduring monument to our generation. Long after the Woolworth Tower has been pulled down to make room for other structures, and perhaps even forgotten, the Mississippi will be flowing quietly between the levees which we are now providing. Perhaps long after the last vehicle has passed over the Brooklyn Bridge these engineering works will be performing their duty. We shall have permanent peace with the Mississippi.

Too long have we been trying to grab more and more land from this river. True enough, we can confine the river to a narrow bed, if we make the levees high enough; but there is a limit beyond which this can go neither safely nor economically. We can, however, use the reclaimed land part of the time. To do this the present plans call for confinement of the river, under normal conditions, to a comparatively narrow bed, and a secondary line of levees is to be built which will take care of the river temporarily in flood times. Engineers are building what are called fuse-plug sections. These are three feet lower than the regular levee, and over them the water will flow when floods begin to menace. They are provided wherever drainage facilities will permit their use. One, forty miles in length, will be provided just below Arkansas.

Another protection device is the so-called spillway. This is a construction of masonry sills which can be operated mechanically to lower the water level when it reaches dangerous heights. The sills can be opened almost instantly. Such spillways are to be provided for the protection of New Orleans.

The basin of the Mississippi has now been thoroughly studied, and in many places it has been found necessary to relocate the levees. This has often resulted in the necessity of cutting across old homesteads. But such is the march of progress and the cost of safety.

The levee forms, for the most part, the only kind of flood protection whose cost is consistent with the value of the land reclaimed. Levees vary somewhat in size and shape, depending on the nature of the soil. For loam, which predominates, they are built with a slant of about one foot in three and a half on the river side and about one foot in six and a half on the land side. The crown is about ten feet across. On the river side the levee is protected by a mat of willow reeds woven into galvanized steel cable. The reeds are spread out on the water and sunk by piling stones upon them. More recently a concrete mat has been devised. This consists of concrete slabs held together with steel cable.

When the work is complete it will constitute the greatest achievement in flood protection that the world has ever known, and there will be no question about its safety. Wherever experts have differed as to the best method to be used at any point, the safe procedure has in every case been followed. Thus does man control the natural forces which threaten him.

Men Killed by Milk Explosions

While it may not always be the unexpected which happens, as has so often been said, nevertheless the unexpected frequently does happen in a way which is very mystifying. If we were to warn workmen of the presence of glycerol nitrate, cellulose nitrate, or of trinitrotoluene, every one would keep at a respectful distance. The very names of these seem to frighten him. But if we were to post up a sign saying "Danger, Flour!" or if we were to warn of the danger of cork, milk, chocolate, or a dozen other materials, we should be laughed at by most men. Have they not used these materials all their lives? They have never seen a milk bottle explode nor a cork suddenly fly to pieces.

It is this attitude which makes it so difficult to guard against explosions of these substances, explosions which take a tremendous toll of life and property every year. How do such explosions come about?

Explosions may be placed in two classes, physical and chemical. A physical explosion is represented in the blowing out of an automobile tire. The wall fails to hold against the physical pressure inside, and a sudden release of the pressure, an explosion, takes place. A boiler explosion due to excess steam pressure is also of this type. A chemical explosion is one in which a chemical action suddenly produces large quantities of gas which build up a high pressure at a very rapid rate. This leads to a physical explosion.

Now any material which will burn, will in

general, produce gas. The rapidity with which the gas is produced depends upon the rate of combustion. If a cork is in a solid piece, as we are accustomed to see it, the combustion can take place but slowly, as the flames must burn their way into the interior of the mass. But suppose we grind the cork to a very fine powder and shake it up in a box filled with air and then set a flame to it. It will explode! Every individual dust particle is surrounded by air containing the necessary oxygen for combustion. Every particle can burn at once. The result is that gas is formed at a very rapid rate, and if the dust is in an enclosed space, the escape of gas must take place with the attendant destruction of the container.

Almost every industry is subject to the dust hazard. Of a number of cases reported, one was due to pyroxylin lacquer dust, resulting from the spraying of automobile bodies; eleven were sulfur dust; four, hard rubber dust; sixteen, starch; nine, sugar; twenty-seven, wood dust; six, cork; two, aluminum; six, fertilizers; three, spice; two, pitch dust; one, rosin; two, powdered milk; two, chocolate and cocoa; two, celluloid; and three, cotton dust. This gives some idea of the diversity of materials subject to this hazard. There is almost no dust which will not burn.

Most of these explosions were caused by hard material getting into the grinders and producing sparks. Next came friction between belts and pulleys, as a cause of the explosions. This produces static electricity, which may produce a spark. Open flames and broken lamp bulbs were also among the causes of these explosions. In one case the spark was due to a broken elevator chain. In another it was caused by sliding boxes along the floor.

Such explosions, difficult to ward against, must be considered a major danger wherever dust exists. And they are usually severe. Dr. David J. Price, of the United States Bureau of Chemistry and Soils, writes:

> The Bureau has obtained records of more than 300 of these explosions. In seventy-eight dust explosions 498 persons were killed and in 106 explosions 878 were injured. In 144 cases the property loss amounted to $39,706,108, an average of nearly $246,590 for each explosion. The economic importance of this problem can be more readily appreciated when it is realized that at least 28,000 industrial plants, employing over 1,324,000 persons and manufacturing products of an annual value in excess of $10,000,000,000, are subject to the hazard of dust explosions.

Battling with Icebergs

With the increased necessity for year-round shipping, with the increased number of water-power electric-generating stations, as well as other year-round activities on main waterways, has come into being a new kind of engineer, the ice engineer. It is his business to break up ice jams which may occur and, in so far as possible, prevent their recurrence. Anyone with a small amount of engineering education will realize the difficulties of such a job. The first part of it, prevention, is not so difficult. An understanding of the flow of water and of the theory of ice formation is frequently all that is necessary to enable the engineer to formulate methods of preventing an ice jam. Once the ice jam is formed the matter becomes decidedly more difficult. Treatment of such a condition usually requires heroic measures. This is because an ice jam usually involves thousands of tons of ice, and because the amount of heat required to melt ice is enormous. To melt ice requires eighty per cent. as much heat as is required to raise the temperature of the resulting water from freezing to boiling temperature. To melt ice is, therefore, clearly not to be thought of. The first recourse, usually taken by the inexperienced, is to blast out the ice with dynamite. This is, in general, out of the question. We all know the great effort required to blast a cut through a mass of rock in railroad or highway construction. It is a process requiring weeks for even a small cut. An ice jam requires immediate relief to avoid possible floods. In addition the ice, being more elastic than the rock, is less easily shattered.

The most successful work that has been done in clearing ice blocks has been accomplished through the use of thermite. The use of thermite is like pouring white-hot steel into a crack in the ice. The molten metal is produced by the action of aluminum and iron oxids. This has a variety of effects. In the first place, the high temperature causes great expansion in the neighborhood of the crack into which it is poured. The unequal expansion at this and other points results in cracking, for the same reason that a cheap glass will crack if hot water is poured on it at one spot. In addition to this effect the disintegration of the water into its components, hydrogen and oxygen, produces an explosive mixture of great violence. It is not thought, however, that this is of great importance, altho it all helps. One of the foremost ice engineers, Dr. Howard T. Barnes of McGill University, Montreal, is of the opinion that the effect is principally due to the transmission of heat rays through the ice. These are finally absorbed along seams and various points of inhomogeneity. Such rays, he thinks, may travel in the ice for some time and set up strains, due to expansion, which are not at once evident. A charge of thermite, when set off, has little immediate effect. It is usually many hours later that the ice begins to crack up. In this way large icebergs have been destroyed, and it is contemplated that further improvements on the method will make it possible to destroy all icebergs which threaten to drift into the ship lanes. The possibilities of this fascinating field of engineering are just beginning to be realized.

Fires that Start Themselves

One of the problems with which man must constantly struggle is that of fire prevention and control. There are few causes of fire which we cannot directly eliminate. And yet we go on having fires, costly in life and in property, daily. It is estimated that among farmers, where the availability of fire-fighting equipment is not great, one-sixth of the net profits of the farmer are wiped out each year by fires.

Among the various causes of fires which are preventable may be mentioned defective chimneys and flues, sparks on combustible roofs, careless use of matches and cigarets, careless handling and storing of gasoline and kerosene, faulty electric wiring, and improper use of electrical apparatus. Among the major causes of fire which can only be listed as semi-preventable, may be mentioned such natural forces as lightning and spontaneous combustion. It is only these latter causes which interest the scientist to any extent.

In the case of lightning the possibility of fire can be almost wholly eliminated by the proper use of lightning rods. These rods, which have long been in use, unfortunately acquired a bad reputation which extended over a number of years, because of fraudulent practises or lack of knowledge. Unscrupulous concerns marketed wholly worthless rods which were not built to the necessary specifications and in many instances constituted a menace. In other cases adequate rods were not properly installed, and as a result were worse than useless. The prejudice which was built up against lightning rods has now been largely removed, and rods conforming to the best electrical practises are being installed in many places, with the result of almost perfect protection.

The problem of spontaneous combustion has not, however, been so well solved. The cause of this is still not well understood. It appears that the first step in the cause of spontaneous combustion is often due to bacterial action. But as this ceases, due to the death of the bacterial organisms at about 70 degrees centigrade, which is far below the point of combustion of the substances in which the fires usually occur, it appears that from here on the action must be chemical, and perhaps catalytic.

Because of the enormous number of barn fires that occur on farms through the spontaneous combustion of hay, the Department of Agriculture of the United States has assigned a staff of scientists to the study of this problem. The best field results that have been obtained so far have come from a study of the Vermont floods in 1927. Many of the farm buildings are in valleys, and during the flood, where barns were not carried away, they were left standing in as much as seventeen feet of water. Fire, under such conditions, would seem to be the last imaginable worry. Yet many fires resulted from just this condition. Hay standing in the barns became wet and, as the dampness favored the bacterial growth, many fires occurred after the waters receded. Barns still standing in several feet of water were burned down to the water's surface.

It appears that hot pockets develop through the action of bacteria. As the temperature rises, secondary chemical reactions set in; these cause air to rise to the surface, and this air, breaking through, creates an upward draft like that of a chimney. The result is a sudden outbreak of intense fire. If the temperature is not raised to the point of ignition it frequently results in charring, and in this way ruining the hay. Similar spontaneous combustion is thought to have been the cause of the destruction of over a million acres of peat bogs in Florida during a single winter.

Man-Made Lightning

The study of lightning, begun by one of the first American scientists, Benjamin Franklin, is now being renewed. The story of Franklin and his kite is a classic, but since his time very little has been done in this fascinating, tho extremely dangerous, field. Perhaps it is the danger which is the cause of this reluctancy to undertake lightning study. At any rate no great advance in our protection against lightning has been made beyond the lightning rod.

In the early days of electric lighting, to have the lights go off was a common experience. It was not difficult in those times to struggle through a half-hour of darkness. The candles were lighted and we did well enough. Now to have the power go off and tie up one of our subways, for example, is a serious thing. Even to stop the elevators in one of our office buildings for that length of time would lead to great inconvenience. Our power must stay on.

One of the greatest causes of interference at the power station is lightning. The methods of protecting the line from lightning are borrowed from the knowledge which has been obtained from lightning rods. In all these years lightning has not been studied first-hand. Realizing this, two of the largest electrical companies in America sent expeditions into the field in the summer of 1928 to study lightning. The results were far from encouraging. One of these expeditions, which planned to study the effects by photographs taken on an instrument known as an oscillograph, obtained but a single picture in the entire season. This picture was taken in but one fifty-thousandth of a second, and figuring the expense of the expedition, cost $75,000. As a result of this and similar disappointments, a new method of studying the problem has been devised. We now use artificial lightning.

We all remember that Steinmetz succeeded in making artificial lightning in the laboratory several years ago. Since that time the voltages possible in the laboratory have steadily grown. The California Institute of Technology at one time had the highest voltage available in the world—1,500,000 volts. This was recently greatly exceeded at the Pittsfield laboratory of the General Electric Company, where a voltage of 3,600,000 was obtained. The next step was taken at the Carnegie Institute of Washington, where, by the use of a Tesla coil, scientists reached a voltage of over 5,000,000 volts, a value which was again exceeded somewhat by the Pittsfield laboratory.

Now these voltages have been taken out of the laboratory for experimental work on the protection of electrical transmission lines. These lines are struck with man-made lightning and the effects observed in order that better methods of protection may be devised. The means of protection thus devised are in turn put to the test of being struck by lightning at our own convenience. We no longer have to spend long and useless hours in the field waiting for a chance bolt of lightning to come our way. We have mastered the lightning.

With these high voltages scientists have the hope of obtaining much information concerning the structure of the atom, and it is also anticipated that x-ray pictures may be taken through an entire building, so powerful would be the rays produced by such a voltage. It is expected that such x-rays would reveal flaws in castings many feet thick, whereas now we can penetrate but a few inches. We shall not only be able to defy the lightning by new protective devices; we shall be able to enslave it for our own uses.

VII

ELECTRICAL SLAVES

Robots that See, Hear, Taste, Smell, Feel, Think, and Talk

THE number of robots which have been introduced, as the result of recent scientific discoveries, has been large. It has always been the desire of man to cast off as much of his work as possible on somebody else's back, and the robot is a particularly desirable victim. One does not have to regard his feelings in the matter. But while robots have but recently been made in a form to resemble in appearance that which we think a robot should have—a sort of squared-off human form—they have nevertheless been with us for some time. Glass-blowing machines, knitting machines, etc., show almost human intelligence. They seem to have brains, even tho they are decidedly one-track brains.

But before we can say that we actually have a robot we must have one which can see, hear, taste, smell, feel, think, and talk. It must exercise judgment. As a matter of fact, we now have robots which will do all these things, altho not all are combined in one robot. Only recently has the robot been given an eye—in the form of a photoelectric cell, a device which changes light signals to electrical ones. This enables the robot to do a great many things. It enables him to measure and match colors more perfectly than can the human eye, it enables him to direct traffic, to count the number of people passing through a gate. The robot so equipped can do all sorts of things in which a difference in color, the cutting off of a light beam, or the production of a shadow, may be made to figure. It can time race-horses, for example, when they are made to intercept a light beam at the finish of the race.

In the matter of hearing, wonders have been accomplished. A robot has been made which in answer to whistles of different pitch can do a great number of things. The thing which is done, of the several possible, is selected by the tone of the whistle. After the job has been done, this robot reports back that such is the case. This particular robot has even been made to answer and take its orders over the telephone. It is called up in exactly the same manner as one calls a person, from any telephone station anywhere. Another robot which has been devised answers to our own language, apparently. In fact, however, it is only influenced by the number of syllables. On one syllable, one impulse, it will perform one duty; on two impulses another, and so on. Thus we have robots that can both see and hear.

Robots have been devised that have a keen sense of smell. These are used where there is danger of accumulation of poisonous gases, and so keen is their sense that they not only warn of the gas on the slightest approach of danger, but state as well the exact amount of the gas present in a given volume. Robots have also been made with a very sensitive touch. One such, a rail-flaw detector, will not only detect flaws in the rail which are external but it exceeds all possible human ability by detecting flaws in the interior of the rail as well. As it moves along the rail it squirts a bit of white paint on every flaw. In the chemical laboratory, also, robots are used for tasting.

It remains only for the robot to talk and think, and this, too, it has done. A robot has been exhibited which answers questions that are asked it. Automatic vending machines now thank the purchaser. In the matter of thinking—the exercise of judgment—we have the case of the traffic robot that is used where there is little side-road traffic. It interrupts traffic on the main road with a red light whenever a vehicle approaches from the side. But should the side-road traffic become heavy, it ceases to function in this manner and throws red and green for equal successive intervals according to the system ordinarily used at crossroads. Whenever the side-road traffic diminishes, it will go back to the original method of traffic direction after a suitable interval.

Thus we have robots which will perform almost any duty ordinarily required of man. And these robots can, in almost every case, do the work better than man himself. So far all these abilities have never been incorporated in a single robot. Perhaps this will never be done. After all, the robot excels in the one thing in which man is weak, monotonous tasks, and for these only a limited ability, requiring at most the use of one or two senses, is necessary.

Robot Locomotive Engineers

With all due respect to the engineers who have made American railroading what it is to-day, who have pulled their trains "through" against adverse conditions, and delivered their passengers and mail on time in spite of the weather, it must be said, nevertheless, that their day is passed. So far as driving the engine is concerned, the engineer is now reduced to a mere automaton himself, and other and numerous automatons do the work he used to do. Bear in mind, however, that we do not refer to him as unnecessary. With the complicated high-power engines which we have to-day he must be a more highly trained man than ever. It is his job to see that this immense power plant on wheels functions properly. But the thrill of driving the engine is over. In a few more years, to all purposes, he might as well be operating a stationary power plant so far as he will be concerned. This is due to the automatic train control that has been introduced.

In a typical automatic system there may be three kinds of blocks. In the first, where full speed ahead can be maintained, the maximum speed may be sixty-five miles an hour for passenger trains, and fifty for freight. If a train exceeds this speed, a whistle sounds in the cab and the brakes automatically set. They cannot be released until the proper speed is reached. This is accomplished by a governor, which is rotated through gears to the wheels. It is like the old steam-engine governor. As it rotates, two balls are thrown farther and farther apart, at the same time pulling up a collar on a shaft. When this reaches a certain point the whistle and brake are operated.

The second type of block is the danger zone. Here the maximum speed will be about twenty-five miles an hour. The governor is automatically changed on entering such a zone to take care of this reduction in speed by a method to be described. A danger zone may be such always or may become one because of the presence of another train ahead. In a caution zone the speed must be tapered down from seventy to twenty miles an hour in 3600 feet. A chime whistle sounds until the lower speed is reached, and if at any time the engineer exceeds the tapered speed a shrill whistle blows and the brakes are set. Every time an engine passes from one zone to another the shrill whistle sounds and must be stopped by pulling down an acknowledging handle. If this is not done in 300 feet the brakes are set.

These various signals and speed changes are set by means of a current of electricity. In a safe section of track the current follows one rail, passes through the axles of the train to the other rail, and back. So long as this goes on a current is induced in a pair of feelers which are held a short distance above the rails in front of the engine. The current is magnified by amplification with radio tubes and holds down the various devices in their operating condition for high speed. If the current is off, as in a danger zone, the various warnings are released. As a broken rail will break the circuit, either this or a burned-out amplifier tube will set the various devices for danger, and the speed must accordingly be reduced.

From this it will be seen that a train might proceed safely with the engineer instructed never to pull the brakes. Unless he must guard against danger at a crossing, it is never necessary for him to do anything but release them after they have been set by the robot which does the real work. The control is almost entirely out of his hands.

Subway Safety

Perhaps nowhere else has the automatic control of trains reached the stage achieved in the New York subways. Here control is carried to the limit. Every car is crowded underneath with suspended automatic safety devices. In all, fifty-six safety devices are used on the subways. Twenty-two of them are to guard against failure of mechanical or electrical devices. Sixteen guard against human error. The remaining eighteen are alarms to give warning when human, mechanical, or electrical agencies are not functioning properly. In the old days of railroading it was thought necessary to maintain a twenty-minute headway for passenger trains. The subways carry thousands of passengers with less than a minute headway. In rush hours the schedule calls for over thirty trains an hour at Grand Central and Times Square. Allowing for stopping time, it is obvious that the trains must travel close together. One must be pulling into the station as the other leaves. Automatic devices control the speed of the train pulling in in accordance with the speed of the departing train. In ordinary running the train leaves behind it a string of danger signals and a row of levers standing up alongside the rail. If the motorman runs by a signal an automatic brake is set by one of these levers. The lights change and the levers fall back out of the way automatically when the train is a safe distance on.

The subway is the first railroad to control che loading of passengers automatically. As long as there is any obstruction the automatic doors will not close. A rubber lap on the edge contains two parallel springs. If one of these is pushed against the other it closes an electrical circuit which prevents the door from closing. Once the door is closed, however, it cannot be opened except by the automatic control system which opens them at the stops. It is also arranged that the power to move the train cannot go on until all doors are closed. Thus the motorman proceeds knowing that all doors are closed, that nothing is caught in them, and that no passenger can open them. The system can be greatly interfered with by those not familiar with it, but this rarely happens. The passengers who use the subway have themselves become automatic and slide in and out with little friction. It is usually visitors from out of town who become annoyed and cause delay. One argumentative visitor caused a serious jam on the whole system by delaying a train for half a minute at Times Square during a rush hour. Trains were held back all along the line, the platforms became crowded, and matters did not straighten themselves out for hours. This type of delay fortunately rarely happens.

With automatic control of the trains, and of the loading of passengers, the subway is able to carry enormous crowds with very few attendants. It is not improbable that in the future men may be entirely dispensed with and the trains operated altogether by robots. Already they have taken over the important job of collecting the fares.

Speeding Up the Railways

Our railroads are rapidly being electrified, because we are demanding greater and greater speeds. In 1829 when the Rocket, competing against three other locomotives, carried passengers at a speed of from twenty-four to thirty miles an hour, speeds of 100 miles an hour were freely predicted. That was because rail transportation, being more expensive at the time than any other, offered no advantage except in speed. As costs were reduced, high speeds were no longer sought. In America, where the distances were large and the roads had to compete with low-priced canal traffic, speed remained something of a factor for many years. But with the canal traffic out of the way the railroads forgot about speed again. Thus the famous locomotive, 999, which holds the speed record, made its

E. K. IV—5

run in 1893, not a period that we think of as the age of speed.

Now that the airplane has come into use we are again demanding speed. This is shown by the popularity of the crack trains that are being run in increasing numbers. It is shown by the combined railroad-airplane schedules which call for connections between day airplane travel and night train travel. The railroads realize in the airplane a serious long-distance competitor and in the bus a serious short-distance competitor. They must speed up.

Now, speed costs money. As a train travels faster and faster the depreciation of the rolling stock and the upkeep of track both increase rapidly. The wind resistance also goes up, and there is a tremendous loss of power due to radiation from the engine. It is these things which have limited our speed for so long.

In operation it is necessary to offset as many of these as we can. Electrification helps. On electrified roads the power plant is stationary and can be operated more efficiently than a power plant moving at high speeds. At low speeds the moving power plant is more economical, as there are no transmission losses. In the beginning of railroading many were of the opinion that the trains would be drawn by cables pulled by stationary engines. Such cable lines are in use on steep grades, but it now appears that they will all be superseded by the invisible cables of electricity.

Our speeds are limited somewhat also by our tracks. As it happens, they are about the best that we know how to build economically. Experiments are being tried out with much longer rails to cut down on the number of joints. Other changes are being considered. We may look forward to electrified roads and much greater speeds in the future.

Talking Movies

It needs no herald to tell us that the talking motion picture is here. It is. And it would seem that every communication engineer in the country is hard at work in this new and fascinating field. It requires the highest developments in the art of communication to make these frozen messages and to reproduce them on the screen. Let us review the process.

To begin with, the communication engineer had to call in the acoustical engineer to help him. In general he became an acoustical expert himself. He had to sound-proof the studios so that absolutely no noise entered from without, he had to still the click of the camera and the hiss of the lights previously used in motion-picture photography. All these are genuine problems.

Having achieved silence, which at this stage

is most certainly as golden in the literal sense as silence ever was, the next problem was to "can" the voices of the artists. In the earliest successes the phonograph record was used. In some systems it is still used. The turn-table had to move in exact synchronism with the film, and the two had to move at constant speed to avoid changes of pitch on the record. This was done by using a constant-speed motor and gearing the turn-table for the record directly to the mechanism which moved the film. If this could not be done they were both moved by synchronous motors. A similar system was used in the reproduction of the film and sound. Since the record must be put on the turn-table and started so as to synchronize with the picture, there is a slight difficulty here. It has been found, however, that they can be out of step by a fraction of a second without its being evident to critical observers.

In other systems of talking motion pictures the sound record is placed on the side of the film which carries the picture. It may be of two types: either it is a black strip (white on the positive) of varying width, or it is one of varying intensity. In the first case the sound is made to vary the width of a slit through which light passes to the film. This is accomplished by picking up the sound and changing its variations to electrical variations by means of a microphone, just as it is done in a broadcast studio.

The electrical variations are used to do the mechanical work of opening and closing the shutter, and the light which passes through sets up the photo-chemical action in the material of the film. Thus we have energy in the form of sound, electricity, mechanical action, light, and chemical action all taking place in recording the sound on the film. Where varying intensities are used, the system is much the same except for the omission of the mechanical shutter. The electrical energy is utilized directly to light a small glow-lamp, the intensity of which varies with the current through it. The sound record on the film is a strip whose intensity varies with that of the lamp.

In reproducing the sound a lamp is placed so that its light passes through the sound record and strikes a photoelectric cell. This cell has the ability to change light variations back into electrical variations. These are amplified by methods common to radio receiving sets and made to operate loud-speakers.

The results which have been attained in this field are truly astonishing, and we may feel assured that we are only on the threshold of a great power in education as well as in entertainment.

Television

Television is an accomplished fact. It is now possible for a man to sit in his home and see events which are happening thousands of miles away. It has been done in trans-Atlantic television experiments. Yet, since television is still in the experimental stage, it has so far obtained but little hold on public interest. In one way it is farther along than most people realize, while in another it is less far along. This self-contradiction lies in the fact that while its progress up to the present has been steady, it has now run into difficulties which appear to have no ready solution. In order to understand this let us look into the method used in television in general.

To begin with, a picture is sent bit by bit in such rapid succession that the eye which receives the picture retains the image of the first bit sent up to the time the last bit appears. The process of viewing the picture or scene to be sent is by scanning it with a powerful beam of light which is made to move over it rapidly. The beam moves over the scene in a manner similar to that in which this page is read. You read one line across from left to right, then repeat on the next, and so on. In like manner a picture is scanned; a narrow strip of light moves successively over adjacent strips. This may also be accomplished by illuminating the entire scene and scanning it by means of a moving lens.

As the light scans the scene, the variations in light and shadow are used to produce a varying current through a photoelectric cell. In this the light variations are changed to electrical variations. The electrical changes can then be amplified and sent out over wires, or broadcast by radio.

When the varying light signals are picked up at the receiving end, they are reconverted from electrical variations to variations in light intensity. They are amplified and sent through a glow-lamp whose intensity varies with the current. This light is spread out on a screen by an inverse scanning process, and so forms the picture viewed.

Some of the mechanical difficulties will be at once evident. It is obvious that the scanning process at the receiving and transmitting ends must be exactly synchronized, otherwise the picture will be greatly distorted. This is accomplished by sending out from the receiving end a synchronizing signal which is picked up and amplified and which automatically keeps the two scanning systems in step. This requires a separate circuit where wires are used, or if two frequencies are used on the same wires, it requires a filter system. In radio television it requires two wave-bands, one for the picture and one for synchronizing.

Starting the two scanning systems at the same time is not important. Failure to do this merely means that the picture will not be properly centered on the screen, and this can be remedied at once by manual control at the receiving end.

The two limiting factors in the system are the photoelectric cell and the reproducing glow-lamp. For suitable operation, at present, intense light is necessary to affect the cell sufficiently for transmission. Pictures illuminated with bright sunlight have been sent, but in general it requires much more light than this. At the receiving end the glow-lamp cannot have its light spread out over more than a few square inches if it is to be clearly seen. Thus we are limited at both ends, and as yet there appears to be no more suitable apparatus in sight than we now have.

Much experimenting has been done with other devices used to change light variations into electrical ones, but these have all met with failure. As a rule they fail because of lag. The electrical response to the light does not come until after a short lapse of time. This voids their use in television, which requires that the device follow the changes at rates up into the thousands per second.

It is somewhat the same thing which limits the receiving end. The lamp used must follow the electrical changes and vary its intensity at this same rate. The glow-lamp is the only device which will do this. Unfortunately, it has low intensity. In a way this can be overcome by using a large number of glow-lamps to form a screen, and as many as twenty-five thousand have been used in this way on a single screen. Each of these requires a separate circuit, which results in costly and complicated apparatus. This is beyond the practical for ordinary use. Thus we have reached a point beyond which there seems no possibility of going at present. There is no reason why we may not soon have motion pictures by television, however. Here intense lights can be used at the transmitting end, and even tho the viewing screen at the receiving end is not large, it can be seen by those gathered around.

Many interesting things have been done with television. A system has been devised for recording the electrical variations on a wax disk similar to that used on phonographs. This disk can be later "played" and the picture of the original scene reproduced. Colored television has been accomplished by the use of two or more glow-lamps, which have complementary colors. The light from both is thrown on the screen at the same time. Noctovision has been accomplished. This consists in scanning the scene with invisible light rays which actuate the photo-electric cell in the usual way and produce the image quite as usual at the receiving end.

Man has always wanted to see and hear at a distance. This has been in evidence ever since he first climbed a tree to look afar. The invention of the telescope gave him his first powerful tool with which he might gratify this desire to some extent. Now comes television, which will allow him to look across continents, around corners, and into dark rooms. When this becomes a commercial success it would seem that at least one of his desires will be thoroughly gratified.

Radio By-products

Obviously we cannot pass over the modern developments of science without some mention of radio. And yet the achievements in this field are so well known to every one that there seems to be but little that one can say that would be information even to the least informed on scientific matters. We have all seen radio develop from the days of the nickel coherer, through the crystal stage, and to the modern vacuum tube. The best we can do, then, is to point out a few of the side developments which the average man may have overlooked.

Consider for example the transatlantic telephony that has become a regular part of our telephone service. This is accomplished by short-wave radio. We may now pick up the receiver in our homes and offices and call over 17,000,000 subscribers in the United States and Europe. When we talk to Europe from the United States the message is carried to the coast, where it is amplified and fed into a broadcast system. By short waves it is carried through the air to England, where it is received by a radio receiver quite different in appearance from those in our homes, but operating on exactly the same principle. Here it is again amplified and fed into the telephone lines.

Wherever there is a small effect, which can be better studied when increased, the methods of radio are employed. It is now common in medical schools to amplify the sound of the heart-beat both for study and for instruction. In this way the human heart can have the sound of its beat so amplified as to rival the noise of the boiler factory.

The methods of magnification which have been developed in radio are also used in the field of television to amplify small changes of light and shadow. They are used to control trains automatically by small current changes in the rails. They are used by the passengers on trains to telephone while the trains are in motion. The signals are broadcast and are picked up by the wires which parallel the tracks.

There is almost no limit to the uses of radio methods. As another example we might cite the use of radio to light the flood-lights of an airfield through the use of an audible signal from an approaching airplane.

Thus the list grows and is being added to almost daily. There are an enormous number of by-products of radio. To find and describe them all in detail would be a task in itself, and no doubt more than a single volume would be required to do it in. We have benefited in many ways not obvious to the radio-broadcast listener.

And while all this has been going on, radio itself has progressed at a tremendous rate. It is a long way from the head sets of a few years ago to the full-volume, life-like reproduction of today, which power amplification and improved loud-speakers have given us.

Rivaling the Sun

The general feeling seems to prevail that we have about reached perfection in the science of lighting. We have been able to build tiny lamps no bigger than a grain of wheat. We have been able to make great flood-lights whose candle-power is rated in the millions. They have been made so bright that they can actually cast a shadow against the sun, altho we must remember that the sun is some 90,000,000 miles away. Because of such achievements we feel that we have come a long way from the days of our grandfathers who used a tallow candle, or from the times of our own parents who used kerosene lamps. In truth we have, and yet our lighting is far from what it should be.

It is true that occasionally there may exist a well-lighted place. But such places are the exception. Close up all the windows in your home so that no light can get in from outside. Then, after being out in the sun for a short period, come in and turn on the lights. The inadequacy of your lighting will be apparent. Why do you not improve it? Because of the cost and also because of the glare. If you were to bring up the intensity to that of out-of-doors it would be unpleasant. Thus our present lighting has much room for improvement. The life of the bulbs is too short; they convert only an insignificant fraction of the energy which goes into them into light, and the light is produced in too small an area, which necessitates great brightness and consequent glare. Our lighting is good only as compared to that of our forefathers.

Our greatest hope for the future is to be found in the glow-type lamps which are now being used to a large extent in advertising signs. These lamps have the great advantage of producing the illumination over the whole of their interior. This reduces the brightness for an equal amount of light, and the glare is diminished. It is also true that these lamps more nearly approach the ideal cold light. For a given amount of energy more light and less heat is produced. But thus far they are less efficient than the ordinary lamp, because of the large electrical leakage due to the high voltage necessary to operate them. This will be overcome by better methods of insulation.

Glow-lamps of this type may be made to operate without any wiring entering the bulb. They will operate through the glass from electrodes on the outside, or they will operate from the changing magnetic field of a coil of wire surrounding them. Thus lamps of this type should eventually be much cheaper to make than are those now in use. They would need merely to be placed between two outside contacts, or in a nest made from a coil of wire. The lamp itself would be as clear as a crystal sphere. There would be no filament to burn out, no base to twist off, no evaporation of a filament to blacken the bulb. None of the things which limit the life of our present lamps would be present.

Recently such a lamp as this, placed on the roof of one of the large electrical laboratories, gave so much light that a newspaper could be read by its aid at a distance of two miles. Why are these lamps, then, not in common use? The answer is, principally, that they have an unsatisfactory color. The color depends on the gas inside. The amber red lamps, so common in advertising signs, contain neon. This gas is chosen because the color stands out well. The blue signs contain mercury vapor. Other colors are due to a mixture of gases or sometimes to the kind of glass used. But thus far a color satisfactory for lighting purposes has not been obtained. Perhaps eventually someone will find the right combination of gases or some other means of making such lamps suitable for home use. Then we may expect to see them come into general use. Because of the red light, given by neon, these lamps are coming into use for signaling, particularly in aeronautics. The red light has a greater fog penetration than equal intensities of white light or light of other colors.

Flood-lighting is another type of illumination that is proving popular. Buildings are floodlighted for advertising or exhibition purposes. Private gardens are being flood-lighted with a soft glow, with spot lights to pick out any particularly beautiful shrub, or group of flowers. Flood-lighting of air-fields is particularly well developed. The ground can now be flooded with light by a single searchlight that will give sufficient illumination for landing as much as three-quarters of a mile from the lamp. The light is spread out into a fan-shape so that none of it is over two feet above the ground. An aviator can fly directly toward such a lamp without being troubled by the glare.

Better and better lighting is becoming prevalent everywhere. It has been found in factories that good lighting not only protects the eyesight and makes happier and steadier workers, but likewise greatly increases the quantity and quality of their output. Few manufacturers have to be persuaded nowadays to bring their lighting up to standard for the sake of the employees. They know that they will be well repaid in output for what may be spent. Nor do the employees resent being speeded up in this way. Not only are they quite unaware that they are able to work faster, but they would be happy to do so if it were pointed out to them. No longer is there the knitting of brows over close work and the after-hours headache. It is one way in which every one benefits.

VIII

POWER

Fuelless Motors

THE public has long since ceased to buy gold bricks. It is some time since the Brooklyn Bridge has been sold. No one will consider for a moment investing in a perpetual motion machine. But men, nevertheless, can still be fooled by the very same thing under its new name—fuelless motor. There is no such thing as a fuelless motor and there never will be, in the proper sense of the word. This statement rests on two laws which are known as the first and second laws of thermodynamics. The first of these says that energy can neither be created nor destroyed, and the second one says that you cannot get energy by a transfer of heat from a cold to a hotter body.

If you ask how we know that these laws are true, the answer is that no violation of them has ever been observed by man. You will undoubtedly admit that you are convinced that a stone will never, of its own accord, start rolling up hill. This is because you are familiar with stones. Those who are familiar with the laws of thermodynamics, through years of association with devices depending upon them for operation, are just as sure that a perpetual-motion

[145]

machine, or in other words a fuelless motor, will never be built.

Perhaps the nearest approximation to free energy we shall ever get is in the waterfall. It is free in the sense that it flows whether we put our turbines there or not. It costs us nothing to get the water to the top of the falls, and its fall produces power. In the same way winds may be said to be sources of free energy. The wind blows whether our windmill is there to make use of it or not. If we are ever able directly to utilize the rays of the sun, we shall have a similar condition.

The only other forces that we have available are the ocean tides and waves (which will be dealt with separately), the earth's changing magnetic field, atmospheric electricity, temperature differences on the earth and in the ocean. In the case of changes of the magnetic field of the earth we have a factor that is negligible except during the relatively rare period of a magnetic storm. Normally the field changes too slowly to produce any power. This has been, nevertheless, the source of many claims by fraudulent inventors. In the case of the atmospheric electricity we have also a source of power which is negligible. It has been estimated that if all the atmospheric electricity over the State of Wisconsin could be collected it would produce, on the average, but twenty kilowatts of power.

POWER

There is as yet no way in which it appears that we shall ever be able to use atomic energy. And yet the stores here are enormous. Dr. W. F. G. Swann, in speaking before the Franklin Institute of Philadelphia, said: "There is so much positive and negative electricity in a cubic centimeter of matter in the substance of the earth, for example, that if all the positive electrons in one cubic centimeter could be collected at one point and all the negative electrons in that cubic centimeter could be collected at another point one centimeter away, the two would attract each other with a force equivalent to 100,000,000,000,000,000,000 tons." Here is room for the imagination to have full play. It is a source which we cannot as yet feel thoroughly assured is not open to us. The prospects for the utilization of atomic forces, however, do not look bright.

Wind-Power

In estimating the power resources of a country, little if any attention is ever given to the wind-power available. We are accustomed to think only of water-power, coal, and petroleum reserves. It is doubtful if a thorough study of the wind resources of even so much as a single locality has ever been made. And yet we know that some localities are regularly affected by strong winds which, if harnessed, would furnish considerable power.

But rather than increasing our use of wind as a power-source, we have been tending in the other direction. Sailing vessels have all but disappeared from our seas. In Holland, the land of the windmill, we are told that electric motors are being installed in their place. Recently a rotor-ship, using the power from the wind in a novel way, was admitted to be a failure after many tests. The wind as a source of power has fallen to a negligible use.

And yet we all know that a sheet of canvas on a boat, with even a moderate breeze, will do the work of a two or three horse-power motor. We know that the farmer uses the windmill to pump water for his animals. This is a heavy duty. Where, then, is the trouble? The answer is in the lack of dependability. The necessity is for an engine which is not dependent on the whims of the weather. It causes too many delays and too much loss of man-time, which is expensive.

In the case of pumping water the windmill does well enough, for it can fill a tank that will last over a calm. This is what is needed if we are to use a windmill for power, a system whereby power can be stored to be used when there is no wind. This could be effected by impounding water on a hillside, where the contour of the land made it possible, or by accumulating electricity in storage batteries. This latter system is no different from that in use on hundreds of farms to store the energy from a gasoline engine for farm lighting. Recently the Air Service has adopted a similar scheme for the purpose of operating signal lights in out-of-the-way mountain regions. The whole device functions automatically. Whenever there is a suitable wind the batteries are charged by the windmill through a generator, and at night the beacon lights are turned on automatically. These lights will function without attention for six months at a time. The only occasion for visiting them at these intervals is to put more water in the storage battery. It is even conceivable that this will also be made unnecessary, the water being provided by rain and allowed to run into the batteries under the control of a float.

At the present time there appears to be a possibility of improving the efficiency of windmills by borrowing from the researches in aeronautics. It would seem that there might be obtained valuable information on the most effective shape for the blades as well as the angles at which they should be held. Also there is no doubt that if we abandoned the idea of directly coupling the wind-power to the machine to be driven, the windmill could be more advantageously located than at present, perhaps on a hill-top, and the power brought to a point where needed, electrically.

There is no doubt that here is an enormous energy reservoir which is going to waste principally because of its lack of reliability. When some convenient and cheap method is devised to compensate for this, the wind, as a source of power, will doubtless come back into favor.

Harnessing the Ocean

Harnessing tides is an ambitious project; and thus far it has not been done. That it will be done in the near future, at least in one case, seems certain. In Passamaquoddy Bay there is a rise and fall of the tide over a range of about twenty-eight feet. The bay, which lies between the province of New Brunswick, Canada, and the State of Maine in the United States, has across it a row of islands and shoals. It is planned to build a dam across this, which would impound the water at high tide and release it later through suitable gates for the generation of power. The cost of developing this project to produce between 400,000 and 500,000 horse-power is estimated at $50,000,000 to $75,000,000. It is thought that eventually as much as 800,000 horse-power could be developed.

In this instance there exists a particularly favorable set of circumstances. Not only is the tide high, but the district is such that uses for this power could be easily developed. The formation of the bay is likewise favorable. There are many other places where the tide is favorable, but something else is usually lacking. Thus at Anchorage, Alaska, the tide is higher than at Passamaquoddy Bay, but no market for the power could be obtained there.

As one sees the rise and fall of a ship with the changing tides one cannot but be impressed with the immense power at work. The difficulty in utilizing this power is one of storage. If we required power only as the tide went out, all would be well, but when power is needed at all times and can be generated only with the fall of the tide, a storage system is essential. At Passamaquoddy Bay this can be taken care of by impounding the water, but not everywhere is the land formation favorable to this. Other systems of storage have been found uneconomical.

In addition to the tides it has been suggested that the battering action of the ocean's waves be harnessed. Commander Lybrandt Smith of the United States Navy has invented a system whereby each wave enters a funnel and by its battering action forces some of the water up into a pipe at the funnel-end. It is prevented from returning by suitable valves. In this way water is raised to a higher level and the energy due to its fall utilized.

When not all of our natural waterfalls have

as yet been developed, and when the cost of power-development by natural falls is approximately the same as generation by coal, Commander Smith's suggestion would hardly seem practical. Added to the usual costs there would be the cost of the installation to raise the water.

In the same way the suggestion of use of the ocean's currents is not feasible. These are no swifter than our inland streams, and the power which could be obtained from their flow would be negligible.

An interesting scheme, which appears to have some promise of practicability, is that of the French scientist and inventor, Georges Claude. M. Claude proposes to use the difference between the temperatures of the ocean surface and the ocean depths. The temperature at a depth of 3000 feet is thirty-five or forty degrees lower than that at the surface. For more than a year M. Claude has had a small experimental plant operating on the Meuse River at a point where the temperature difference between the top and bottom is about forty-six degrees. Water at the lower temperature is pumped through a pipe insulated against heat. He estimates that the rise in temperature of the water brought up from below will be about one degree because of heat-leakage through the pipe.

Recently the plant on the Meuse, which generates fifty kilowatts of energy, has been moved and is to be set up sixty-two miles east of Havana. Here a long corrugated metal pipe will run out to sea and to the ocean's bottom. It is felt that this is a nearly ideal place to try out the experiment, as the system lends itself primarily to the generation of power in the tropics and especially on the tropical islands out at sea. If this station proves successful, M. Claude visualizes, first, a series of such power stations to generate about 15,000 horse-power each, and ultimately, stations of as much as 150,000 horse-power.

Heat from Cold

Somewhat similar, and yet half as far apart as the poles, is the suggestion of Dr. H. Barjot as compared to that of M. Claude. Instead of utilizing temperature differences of the ocean, Dr. Barjot proposes to utilize the temperature difference between the atmosphere and water protected by a surface of ice. Thus while M. Claude's plan is adapted to the tropics, that of Dr. Barjot is suited to the arctic regions.

Ordinarily we use coal to produce steam, and cold water to condense the steam, which is used over again. According to Dr. Barjot's plan we would use the heat of the water under the ice to vaporize a substance, such as a hydrocarbon, and this would be condensed by frozen brine. Some material such as propane, butane, or petroleum by-products, now largely wasted, might be used as the working substance to replace the water of the ordinary boiler. The vapor at one atmosphere would expand to a pressure of about one-fifth of an atmosphere and be used to run a low-pressure turbine. Turbines to work on pressures of this order of magnitude are already available.

The condensing material, frozen brine, could be obtained by flooding a large surface of the ice with brine and harvesting this frozen material. This would be much less expensive than mining coal and transporting it over long distances. When water is kept in motion at a temperature below the freezing point, ice does not form on its surface. Instead, ice crystals form throughout the body of the water. Such ice is known as frazil ice. As much as ten per cent. of the water can actually be ice and yet the flow goes on. It is suggested that this fact might be made use of and that the brine might be constantly circulated over a long path on the ice surface and the frazil constantly skimmed out at a point near which it would be used. This would greatly cut down the cost of harvesting the low-temperature material needed in the process.

Thus we have answered the old question as to what is going to happen to the earth's inhabitants when the sun begins to cool and we reach the last and final ice age. As long as there exists a temperature difference, regardless of how low it may be, man will be able to generate power, and if he can do this he can at least keep himself from freezing, and can supply his food by hothouse methods.

"There is a curious paradox in the process," says Dr. Barjot. "The colder the weather the more efficient the process, and so the more power (which can be turned into heat) is given.

"Science could in this manner conquer the polar regions," he says, "and open up those barren lands to civilization to add their wealth to mankind, thus enabling more human beings to live."

Power from the Earth's Interior

One of the old desires of man has been, in some manner or another, to tap the enormous power resources which must be tied up in the interior of the earth in the form of heat. It has been found that the temperature as we go down into the earth, especially in volcanic regions, increases very rapidly, and there is every reason to believe that inexhaustible stores of energy exist, which we could use if only we could find some way of tapping them. It is not generally known that this has already been done in at least two places on the earth's surface.

One of the two places where the natural heat of the earth's interior is used for power is in

Tuscany, Italy. Here there is a valley which seeps with hot springs and steam coming from the ground. About twenty years ago Prince Ginori Couti conceived the idea of utilizing this steam as a direct source of power. He piped it into the cylinder of an engine which he succeeded in running, and which has been in use ever since.

A few years ago Mr. J. D. Grant, who knew nothing of the Italian venture, took a lease on a piece of property in California, strikingly similar to that in Italy, and began to develop steam wells for power purposes. Had he been familiar with the Italian case he would doubtless have been discouraged, for the temperatures and pressures at the ground-level were less in the California area than in Tuscany.

Mr. Grant developed one of these wells by boring in a manner somewhat similar to that used in oil-well construction, and as the temperature and pressures of the steam increased with depth he was able to develop a steam well which operated a small turbine and supplied a neighboring hotel with light and power. Using the power available from the first well, he has subsequently drilled five others, which vary in depth from 500 to 650 feet. The temperature in these wells, when they are closed, has been found to vary from 290 to 374 degrees Fahrenheit. As this is considerably above the boiling point, we have a superheated steam. This is a great advantage in power generation. The pressure in the wells was found to vary from 60 pounds per square inch to 275 pounds per square inch. The output of steam is from 1,500 to 52,000 pounds per hour. There seems to be no diminution of the capacity of these wells to produce power over the time they have been in existence.

While wells of this type are not at all likely to become an important source of power, they offer an opportunity for interesting speculation. Mr. E. T. Allen, who has investigated these wells under the auspices of the Carnegie Institution, writes:

> The existence of such an underground reservoir supplying amounts of steam of this magnitude is not only at variance with the known facts of geology; it is also opposed to the semi-arid climate of the region and its scanty store of ground water. The steam must take its rise in a deep-seated source, since its pressure and temperature and the magnitude of the flow increase with the depth of the well. It may be said that the evidence shows that the steam originates in a great mass of molten or partially fluid rock, similar to molten lava in its properties, buried at an unknown depth in the crust of the earth. One reason for this conclusion is that all types of igneous rock, when heated to redness, give out large volumes of steam that is always associated with small amounts of gases as natural as steam is.

Thus, whether these wells ever become of commercial significance or not, they have at least added to our knowledge of geology. Perhaps it will be the inspiration from them which will eventually cause someone to risk the fabulous sums necessary to reach commercially valuable temperatures by straight boring—if we do not in the meantime reach these temperatures through our oil wells, which are of ever-increasing depth. The center of the earth may be our ultimate great power source.

Rockets for Motive Power

The use of rockets for motive power has long been scorned. And there are those who, in spite of the recent decided successes, still treat the subject of rocket propulsions lightly. In fact, they do not admit that the recent experiments with rockets were successes, but rather feel that they have proved the impracticability of rockets for propulsive purposes.

The experiments with the automobile known as the Opel, not long ago, which finally led to the complete demolition of the vehicle by explosion, are not taken seriously. The use of the rocket sled on Lake Starnberg by Max Valier, however, led to considerable success. He reached speeds with this sled of approximately 249 miles an hour; and yet his work received scant notice. The sled did its work so easily that there was apparently nothing spectacular to report. The rocket which was sent off by Prof. Albert H. Goodard in the summer of 1929 was considered by many as a great joke, a complete dud. Nevertheless, it apparently did exactly what Prof. Goddard expected it to do. It careened through the air with great noise and landed a quarter of a mile away. It was neither a failure nor the climax of many years of experiment. He was trying out a new liquid explosive and no doubt gained considerable information from this experiment. More recently we have learned of a successful flight over a short distance, in Germany, by a rocket-driven airplane.

Whatever the critics of this mode of propulsion may say, the fact remains that rockets actually have driven various kinds of vehicles over short distances. And it should be kept in mind that not only is the mode of operation at the present time crude in its development but that also it has been applied to vehicles designed for other types of power plant. We have as yet not even begun to change the design to suit the power used. The critics should also take time to recall that there are still many of their kind living who said that an airplane was an impossibility. They now must listen to the drone of the motors of airplanes daily. And it should be remembered, too, that their criticism was much more justified than is that of the rocket critics.

The airplane was something much newer and more revolutionary than is the rocket.

If we look back into history we find that Hero of Alexandria is said to have invented an engine on the rocket principle, 2000 years ago. This was simply a large metal sphere with two bent spouts. The sphere was arranged so that it could rotate. When water in the sphere was boiled the steam escaping from the nozzles caused the sphere to be set in motion. No less a person than Sir Isaac Newton invented a steam engine which was to move by the reaction of steam shooting from an exhaust in the rear. And, as a matter of fact, this is exactly the idea used in our steam turbines to-day. The rotor moves because of the reaction of steam against blades.

One of the great advantages of the rocket is that it does not require a material medium in order to move. A ship moves because of the reaction of its propeller against the water. In the same way an airplane pushes against the air. But in the case of the rocket the motion is the direct reaction against the gases expelled. Thus a rocket will move through space completely devoid of all matter. Because of this fact, those who would visit the moon or other planets have always based their hopes upon it, and it is this which has given the rocket a bad start. Those who work with it are usually looked upon as visionaries bent upon some interstellar voyage. This has kept many serious people, who did not wish to lose their friends, out of the field.

Whether we reach the moon or not, it is true that we should be able to reach much higher points in our atmosphere, by the use of such rocket-propelled airships, than we have heretofore. The height which a dirigible can reach is very limited because of the decrease in lifting power as the atmosphere becomes more rare. The height which an airplane can reach is limited by the lessening efficiency of the propeller against the thin atmosphere, by the loss of buoyancy, and by the freezing up of engine parts at the high, cold altitudes. As the rocket goes higher it has the tremendous advantage that the air resistance is reduced without loss of power. At great heights in the atmosphere it should be theoretically possible to travel by rockets at enormous speeds with very little expenditure of power.

We may confidently expect to see considerable advance in the use of rockets in the near future. The one thing which acts as a detriment to their use at the present time is the lack of methods of controlling the combustion. When this is solved, the rocket as a motive power has a clear road ahead.

Diesel Engines

In 1921 only 330 Diesel engines were built in the United States. By 1925 the number built in a year had reached 4101. What it will be for 1930 or 1940 no one can tell, but it is safe to say that it will be many times this figure. The Diesel engine is gaining ground at a tremendous rate, and the number of uses to which it is being put is also on the increase. Mr. Julius Kuttner, oil-engine expert, writes:

> Some of the output finds its way into the pumping stations of oil transport lines, while the remainder is applied to industrial uses too numerous to mention and to the propulsion of boats and ships. There are now thirty-five Diesel-engine-driven railroad locomotives in the United States, and one airplane. The one-hundred-passenger British airship R-100 will be propelled by five Diesel engines. More ships are now being built with Diesel engines to propel them than vessels with steam power.

What is the cause of this rapid rise in the use of Diesel engines? The answer is in their efficiency. Using the highest compression possible in the gasoline engine, the efficiency has not been raised much above twenty-five per cent. This means using the highest-grade fuel and having the entire engine operating under the most favorable conditions. Steam engines do not exceed twenty per cent. efficiency and usually run somewhat below this. Diesel engines regularly attain an efficiency of thirty per cent. using only low-grade furnace oil. That is the secret of their popularity.

This high efficiency is due to the method of applying the fuel. The oil is not mixed with air before going into the cylinders, as in the gasoline engine. The air is injected into the cylinder free from fuel, and is there compressed to about eight times the pressure used in gasoline engines. Then the fuel is injected and is burned because of the high temperature to which the air has been raised by compression. In such a system there is no danger of preignition, from the high temperature of compression, with the consequent knocking, which takes place in the gasoline engines. It is because of this that the high pressures and consequent efficiencies are possible. Also it is to be noticed that the electrical ignition system is completely done away with. This avoids any possible failure from that source and adds greatly to the reliability of operation.

In the past much effort has been directed toward making these engines in sizes small enough for truck operation. Because of the necessity for outside-pressure apparatus, and because of the weight per horse-power needed where such high compressions are used, they have been too heavy for trucks. Now, however, we have Diesel-

driven airplanes. The Diesel used in this case
weighs less than three pounds per horse-power.
The reduction has been accomplished by firing
the charge nearly on dead center. In this respect
the design flies in the face of previous engineering opinion; for it was thought that the weight
would have to be greatly increased to take care
of the tremendous strain which would result
from so firing the charge. This has not been the
case. Thus we have the first flying Diesel. The
advantage of such an engine is decided. It gives
a twenty per cent. increase in flying range,
abolishes all ignition dangers due to the failure
of the electrical system, removes the fire hazard
of the gasoline, and ends electrical interference
with radio signals.

There is a possibility that eventually the
Diesel will completely replace our present gasoline engines and most of our small steam plants.

The Trend in Railroad Locomotives

Perhaps the casual observer would say that
there have been but few changes in railroad
engines since he was a boy. Possibly they are
bigger to-day, but that is about all that he sees.
As a matter of fact, there have been such great
changes in locomotives in the last ten years that
any engine older than this must be considered
obsolete.

The railroads, with a fixed price set on their

services and the cost of labor and materials advanced, must operate economically. No longer can an engine be gradually shoved from one type of service to another, finally reaching the branch lines of the road as its age increases. To make a profit on the branch line it is now necessary to use an engine designed for its own particular work; each one is a tailored job. It will be efficient on one particular job, but may be far from efficient on others. This accounts for the enormous expenditures that are being made by the railroads for locomotives. One road bought fifty new engines in a single year, to be used entirely to draw its fast passenger trains. These cost about $90,000 each, or a total of nearly $5,000,000. They maintain the schedules with greater speed and economy. The old engines were doing the job, but the decreased cost of operation of the new ones is apparently great enough to offset the original expense.

In 1905 the heaviest engine purchased weighed 355,000 pounds and had a traction of 71,600 pounds. In 1915 these figures were 485,000 and 103,000 pounds respectively. By 1925 the weight had increased to 594,940 pounds and the tractive power to 127,500 pounds. This means more than is evident on the face of it. There is not only the question of increased efficiency of the engine to be considered, but the railroad engineer must ask himself many other questions. Will our present rails and road-bed carry this engine? What will it do to the cost of the upkeep of the road-bed? Will it be necessary to strengthen our bridges, to increase the clearance of our tunnels, to lengthen our turntables? There are all these and many similar questions to be gone into.

The process, then, is somewhat like this: The locomotive builder is asked to draw up preliminary plans for an engine of a certain weight and power, to be used in a class of service for which it is evident that an engine of that type would be efficient. When these plans are in hand, the entire road must be gone over to find what new problems this engine will introduce. If it appears that they can be made at a reasonable cost, then the plans for the engine are worked out in greater detail by a joint committee of engineers representing the railroad and the builder. Every operating feature of the engine will be known before it is built, and its total weight will also be accurately determined. While it is being built the necessary changes on the railroad are being made.

The future of the railroad also must be considered—the possibilities of future electrification, the possibilities of elimination of grades, the possibilities of relocating part of the line. Every precaution must be taken to guard against the possibility of the engine becoming obsolete because of changes in the road itself or because of changes in competing lines. These are the things which guide the evolution of the locomotive.

Our Power Resources

It is estimated that only four per cent. of the power used in the United States comes from water-power, that the soil yields six per cent. in firewood and three per cent. in power from farm animals. This accounts, altogether, for thirteen per cent. of the power used. Neglecting minor sources of power, such as the wind, this means that the other eighty-seven per cent. must come from the consumption of irreplaceable natural resources, coal and oil.

For many years past we have heard a cry of diminishing oil resources. Mr. Thomas Reid, writing in *Mining and Metallurgy,* said: "As long as I can remember I have been hearing that our petroleum resources were in imminent danger of speedy exhaustion, and yet the yearly out put is now of the same order of magnitude as the total resources were once estimated, with the cry of overproduction the loudest it has ever been. Tapping ever progressively deeper and deeper sources of supply has produced this result." To this factor must also be added the new methods of prospecting by sound, radio, etc.

But of course, you say, this cannot go on;

there must be a depth beyond which we shall find it impossible to drill. Discounting the possibility of finding commercial temperatures at these depths—that is, of obtaining power direct from the heat of the earth—we still have little cause for worry. We have already found a method of getting gasoline from our coal mines through the hydrogenation of coal. It is generally agreed that our coal resources will last us for centuries hence. By that time we may have devised a method of getting energy direct from the sun. Future generations may laugh at our laborious method of digging coal out of the ground and transporting it for miles, when clean sunshine is right at our doors, if we but knew how to use it.

Plants are another source of fuel, which must not be overlooked. We may be able to grow a new crop of fuel for engines each year, just as we used to grow a new crop of fuel for animal power. Alcohol can be made from any plants by fermentation, and internal combustion engines to burn alcohol have been available for some time. At present there is little incentive to use such engines because of the higher cost of the fuel required for them. In some of the sugar-raising countries, however, where quantities of molasses are available from which alcohol can be readily made, one notes a definite attempt to encourage the use of this fuel through import taxes on gasoline and on gasoline-burning motors. This may lead to great improvements in alcohol engines.

The introduction of the Diesel engine, which can use a much greater proportion of the fuel taken from oil wells, will also tend to prolong the life of our petroleum resources. Not only will the Diesel operate on low-grade fuel, but at the same time its efficiency is considerably above that of the gasoline motor.

With the improved methods of pumping oil many old wells are again producing as heavily as they did in the so-called golden days.

All these things are working in our favor, and while, for the sake of decreased cost to ourselves, it is desirable to use these natural products with all possible efficiency, it does not seem that their conservation for future generations is at all necessary. The wants of the future generations, indeed, are quite obscure to us. If we denied ourselves the use of natural resources for their sake, we should be like the miser who ate only rotten apples all his life, refusing to use one that might keep for another day.

IX

PUTTING WAVES TO WORK

Secret Signaling

A FAVORITE use of light waves has been for secret signaling. For this purpose we have at hand a great variety of radiations, starting with radio and going on down to the short waves of the x-ray. Most of these radiations, however, are wholly unsuited for secret communication. The radio offers little privacy, and radiation in the ultra-violet, and on down to the x-radiation, is too readily absorbed by the air to be of any service. This limits us to the visible and to the infra-red. Of these two possibilities the latter has been a great favorite, since besides the quality of invisibility it has the additional advantage of passing very readily through fogs. The question then becomes one of detection. Since it has a considerable heat effect, this has been used as a means of detection. Instruments can be made so sensitive as to be used to measure the heat from the most distant stars. In signaling they are of little use, however, as it is the changes which must be measured, and these occur too rapidly in useful signaling for such devices to follow. The most useful thing so far found has been the red-sensitive crystal. Molybdenite is one of these. It has the characteristic of producing an electrical current when the rays strike it. The chief difficulty is that the crystals become fatigued on exposure, their sensitivity rapidly falling off beyond the point of usefulness.

In the end we are driven back to the use of visible rays for the purpose of secret signaling. We find that the best method is to use a light beam in which changes can be made which those not properly equipped cannot detect. Thus one method is to use a bright light and send our signals by placing before it, at the proper code intervals, a thin gelatin film of the type used to filter out the red in photography. This produces a change of intensity so slight that it cannot be detected with the naked eye. If, however, one is supplied with a deep-blue filter, principally transparent to the violet, and views the light through this, interposition of the red filter produces near darkness and the signals can be read with ease. Since the number of possible filter combinations is very large, one has a fair chance to escape detection by even the most persistent inquisitor.

Polarized light has also been used in signaling. Normally light is thought of as vibrating in all planes at right angles to the direction of the beam. The directions of vibrations might be likened to the directions indicated by the bits of tinsel on a string of Christmas tinsel, the length of the tinsel representing the direction of the light ray. If we were to take an iron and press this tinsel flat, that would represent one kind of polarized light. It would be plane polarized. It is possible also to produce circularly or elliptically polarized light. Detection of changes in polarization depend upon knowing what changes to expect and being provided with suitable apparatus to detect them. This then becomes a method of secret signaling.

Another method is found in the use of very restricted beams. Such beams can best be produced by placing a small lamp, such as a flashlight, at the focus of a telescope, and burning it at overvoltage to produce great brightness. A large lamp is undesirable, as only a small part of the filament can be at the focus in any case, and the rest may give light that spreads. When properly arranged, a beam only a few feet wide will be produced even at a distance of many miles. Unless an individual is directly in the beam he can see nothing. In use the sender, looking through the telescope, focuses it on some predetermined object, such as a particular pane in a window. The individual at the receiving ends looks for it at that spot. All is then in readiness to send a code message by interposing a screen.

Colored Motion Pictures

Color photography dates back to 1861. It was at that date that Clerk Maxwell first exhibited a colored picture before the Royal Institution. His method was based upon the fact that white light can be split up into three primary colors —green, blue, and red. When these are combined, white light is produced. Maxwell took three pictures of the same object, one through a filter of green liquid, another through a red, and a third through a blue filter. He projected all three of these, superimposed, upon a screen. The result was a picture colored approximately like the original. This is difficult to accomplish with any fidelity, because of the difference in sensitivity of the photographic plates to different colors. It required exposures of different lengths. At present, however, plates are made which are of nearly equal sensitivity throughout the spectrum, and cameras have been made which expose the three plates at one time. Motion pictures using this plan require that three films be used and be projected synchronously. This is so difficult of accomplishment that a compromise has been made and but two colors used. In this case they may be put on the opposite sides of the same film.

The first advance on this was to combine the three plates into one by placing before the plate

used a colored filter ruled with the primary
colors in very fine lines. In projecting, these lines
had to be in the some position relative to the
plate as they were when the picture was taken.
This was difficult to do, as may be imagined.
The difficulty was overcome in the Lumière
process. Here the fine ruling was replaced by
colored transparent starch-grains which were
sprinkled over the plate. These remained on the
plate after development, so that they constituted
a permanent filter, always in place.

The Lippman process avoids the use of filters
altogether, utilizing instead the interference of
light waves. It is theoretically a perfect system,
but in actual practise is not satisfactory. It sug-
gests a possibility which might be developed in
the future, however. In this system the plate
used is backed by a mirror surface which turns
the light waves back upon themselves. These,
since they interfere in such a way as to produce
standing waves in the emulsion, cause the film
to be reduced in layers upon development. When
viewed at the proper angle, after development,
these striations filter out all but the color which
produced them, and we have a colored picture
similar to the original scene.

Undoubtedly the most practical system so far
devised is that which is now employed in amateur motion-picture systems. This scheme is more
nearly analogous to the finely ruled filter than

to any other. A large filter composed of but three large segments of the primary colors is placed before the usual motion-picture camera. This splits the light from every object before the camera into the three colors that make up white light. Now, the film on which this light falls is ribbed like corduroy, the ribs running the length of the film. Each rib constitutes a tiny cylindrical lens running along the film. When the light from the filter reaches these ribs, since each color comes from a slightly different direction, it is focused in a narrow strip on the emulsion side of the film. The emulsion side is opposite the corrugated side and is away from the lens. When the film is developed there will be a series of strips, each of which has been exposed to but one color. These strips will be alternately red, green, and blue, just as if a colored, ruled filter had been placed before the film. Each rib will have produced such a series of three strips.

When the film is projected, the process is the reverse to that described. The light retraces the path it took on exposure. The same filter is used.

While the system would appear ideal, it is still of little value to the professional. One of its greatest drawbacks is that only one copy of the picture is produced, the original, whereas a producer requires several hundred. Also the intensity of light produced is so small as to limit the projection to a small screen suitable only for amateur use. Perhaps these objections will eventually be overcome and our present colorless motion pictures will become extinct almost overnight, as has the silent picture.

X-rays Now Work Overtime

The x-ray has been of so much value in the hospital that it is thought of almost entirely as a hospital tool. That is where most people come in contact with it. But its use is far more general than we realize. It has found its way into many industrial uses and is constantly pushing the frontier farther back.

The industrial uses of the x-ray are in general very much like its hospital uses—to examine the interior of things which it is not possible or desirable to dissect. Thus it has come to be used for the examination of welded joints, for examining castings for blow-holes or inclusions, and so on. In such cases it is obvious that the x-ray has the advantage over other methods of examination in that the object is not destroyed or injured in any way. During the war the x-ray was used to examine the castings intended for shells. The defective castings were thus sorted out and much time and labor, which would have been used to machine down the defective casting to proper dimensions, was thus saved.

The x-ray has also been used a great deal to examine the condition of assembled objects. During the war, when much wood of inferior grade had to be used in airplane construction, the x-ray was used to find defective gluing, grub holes, or resin pockets. The x-ray has been used to examine the condition of wiring inside the electrically heated jackets worn by aviators, to search bales of cotton for contraband at the customs offices, to determine the location of plumbing in the walls of buildings, to examine the interior of golf balls, and to test the construction of shoes. The list is almost an indefinite one. Any ingenious person can think of many things which could be advantageously examined in this way. He will find that nearly everything up to the equivalent of about three inches of steel has been so examined, and in many cases this is being done as routine inspection.

In addition to this valuable shadowgraph work, the x-ray is being used to study the crystal structure of materials. With its aid the engineer can look inside the actual structure of metals and note their atomic arrangement. He can decide which atomic arrangement gives the greatest strength, greatest hardness, greatest elasticity, and so on. Melting-points and magnetic properties are also dependent upon the atomic structure. These, too, are open to the inspection of the trained metallurgist through the use of the x-ray. He can, in effect, walk around inside the metal and determine its characteristics just as a bridge engineer might examine the construction of a bridge.

Recently the x-ray has come into use to examine into the authenticity of paintings which are offered to collectors as works of old masters. The pigments used a few centuries ago were mostly of mineral origin and therefore opaque; whereas to-day anilin derivatives are largely used. These newer paints are much more transparent to the x-ray than are those formerly used. The application of the x-ray to the examination of such pictures makes it possible to decide almost certainly as to the probable date of the painting. In this way the ones with fraudulent pretensions are detected, and on the other hand the x-ray has in some cases revealed great value beneath an unpromising exterior. The old master's canvas had merely been painted over for use a second time. The x-ray has now become a permanent part of the equipment of most museums. It is invaluable in the examination of old treasures which could not otherwise be examined without injury.

Such use of x-rays is comparatively recent. X-rays have been so tied up with medical work that their other uses seem to have escaped notice. It is a new field filled with interesting possibilities.

PUTTING WAVES TO WORK

The Photomicrograph—the Police of the Metals

In addition to the frequent use of the x-ray to examine the crystal structure of metals, there has also come into use the photomicrographic method. These two methods are not competitive; they are supplementary, for while the x-ray examines a group of perhaps a score of molecules the photomicrograph takes in the area covered by an enormous number. The use of the x-ray might be likened to the examination of this page, or a single letter on it, with a magnifying glass, whereas, in comparison, the use of the photomicrograph would correspond to the examination of a pile of bricks with the eye. And if we use low-powered magnification on our photomicrograph it corresponds more nearly to reconnoitering a territory with an airplane. Thus there is a place for each of these methods.

In examining a piece of metal with the photomicrograph we are merely taking a greatly magnified picture. The method is to polish off the metal very carefully and then etch it with acid. When examined microscopically, it reveals numerous opaque crystalline forms standing out from it. The first examination is low-powered and gives a general view of that part of the surface. If, on this, there appears anything that looks suspicious, it is examined separately under much greater magnification. We have located our pile of bricks, so to speak, from the air; we now descend to examine them.

But why should anyone wish to do this? To make better metals for our daily use. The properties of metals depend almost wholly upon crystal structure. This can be varied in many ways, but particularly by heat treatment. Just what this should be is determined by experience. Suppose we find that a metal is weak. We examine it and find a particular crystal structure. It is safe to assume that this particular crystal form is undesirable, and so we shall try to avoid it. Thus we come to know at once the forms which are desirable for different purposes. The so-called weak metal may be weak in tensile strength, but it may stand much bending. Different properties are associated with different crystal structures.

Iron, by itself, is in general rather weak. It is relatively soft, easily bent, and of low tensile strength. But put some carbon with it and it becomes steel. It is harder and much stronger. The same result is accomplished, in a more pronounced fashion, by putting vanadium in the metal. Iron can be made tougher yet softer, or harder and more brittle, by such methods, at will. It can also be made stronger without the brittleness. Its properties can be made almost what we want them to be—within limits. But it requires care. If the carbon put in is not well distributed, the effect is lost. If the carbon is in a chunk large enough to make up an entire cross-section of a piece of metal, it is obvious that the metal would snap off at this point with the slightest strain. The photomicrographic method tells us how well the distribution has been made. And, knowing the effect on this distribution of various kinds of heat-treatment, the product can be varied at will. The manufacturer now keeps a constant check on his product by this method.

A few years ago it was not at all uncommon to see an automobile by the side of the road with a broken rear axle. Such a thing is never heard of to-day. The manufacturer is no longer guessing as to the strength of this part of his car. He knows that every rear axle he turns out is a good rear axle and exactly like all the others in strength. He knows this from constant tests, tests in which the photomicrograph plays an important part.

Prospecting by Radio

In no field has the introduction of scientific methods brought about more of a revolution than in that of prospecting. The days of the old-fashioned prospector who went along chipping off bits of rock here and there in the hope of a valuable strike are not only numbered, they are actually over. No longer will the hit-and-miss method, so common for years, yield the results which modern business demands. The lone prospector has given way to tractor-trains and airplanes which disturb alike the stillness of the north in their quest for metals and the dusty plains of the south in the search for more oil.

The methods which are now used in prospecting are the seismographic, the magnetic, the gravitational, and the electric. In the first of these, the seismographic, a large charge of dynamite is buried in the earth and set off. Its effect is measured by a seismograph placed at some distance away. As the time required to travel is an important factor, a modern broadcasting method is used to determine this. Sending equipment is set up near the scene of the explosion, and receiving equipment near the seismograph. When the explosion occurs the signal is at once received at the seismograph end, and the time which elapses from then until the sound has reached the seismograph through the ground is measured. To the experienced this means a great deal concerning the nature of the intervening ground. So important is this method of prospecting believed to be that the government has set aside a special wave-band for this purpose.

The magnetic method is useful principally in the search for magnetic materials, but as all metals have either a greater or a lesser permeability than the surrounding earth, much can be learned of the substructure of the earth by map-

ping the magnetic field of the region. This is
done by first making a map and then marking
on it, at many locations, the directions in which
a magnetic needle points. The marked map, of
course, requires interpretation by experts.

The gravitational method requires that we
actually weigh the earth. An instrument of ex-
treme sensitivity, called the gravity balance, is
used for this purpose. A movable part of the
instrument is attracted by the earth beneath it,
the degree of attraction depending upon the
density of the earth's crust at that point. Inclusions of metal thus affect the instrument. So
sensitive is this device that the presence of a
person in its vicinity will throw it completely
off in its measurements. In use it is set up in a
protecting tent or other shelter, to shield it from
winds, and is left to make its record photo-
graphically. Examination of the resulting photo-
graph can be made at leisure.

The direct electrical method consists in bury-
ing in the ground two terminals of a high-poten-
tial machine, such as an induction coil. These
are buried at some distance apart. Then, by the
use of a searching coil, the electrical field at a
great many points in the vicinity of these buried
terminals is measured. These intensity measurements are plotted out on a map of the region
and points of equal intensity joined with a line.
The shape and density of these lines on the map

determine the nature and location of deposits
which may be underground.

This does not mean that the trained geologist
no longer has a place in the search for mineral
deposits. He is as valuable as ever. To find a
needle in a haystack one must first locate the
haystack. Obviously we cannot feel our way over
the entire country with the sensitive methods of
the geophysical prospector. The geologist must
point out first the promising places to look.

Sound Waves and Architecture

One might expect that the study of sound
would date back beyond the study of any other
physical phenomena. Perhaps it does, and yet
the satisfactory application of principles known
for years has been accomplished only recently.
We do not have to stretch our memories much to
remember the squeaky phonographs on which
we heard a distorted recording of Caruso. They
went into the discard scarcely five years ago.
Now, when we hear one of these in the home of
some friend who has either become deadened to
its scratchings or whose musical ear never ex-
isted, we wonder that we did not toss our old
machine into the scrap-heap the day after it was
purchased. The change has been brought about
by an application of acoustical principles.

With this change in our graphophones, and in
our radios, has come also a change in the con-

struction of rooms and buildings where sounds are produced for enjoyment. This includes our auditoriums, our broadcast studios, our sound-picture studios.

One of the first phenomena to be dealt with in properly constructing an auditorium or studio is that of reverberation. If one makes a sudden sound in a large vacant room the sound will be found to persist for some seconds. One might produce such a sound by clapping the hands sharply or by dropping a plank. The length of time which the sound persists is known as the period of reverberation. This period should be neither too long nor too short. If it is too long the sound of a voice is confused—one syllable carries over into the next. The speaker is understood with difficulty. If the period of reverberation is too short, the room is said to be dead. There is a hushed sense which is most unpleasant. One finds the room depressing; one is inclined to speak in whispers.

Investigations have been made to determine the most favorable time of reverberation. It is found that when a room is intended for music the period can be longer than when it is intended for speech. It is desirable to have some of the sound of one note carried over into the next. But in speech to have one syllable carried over into the next makes both quite impossible to understand.

Recently there have been perfected a number of sound-absorbing building-materials. With these, whose coefficients of absorption are known, it is possible to construct a building whose period of reverberation may have any desired value. These materials are also useful in blocking off outside noises.

Sometimes in a very large auditorium echoes become a serious problem. Whenever it is possible for a sound to travel from the speaker to the auditor over two paths, which differ from each other in length by seventy-two feet or more, the time lag of the sound over one path, as compared with the other, is sufficient to cause one syllable to arrive via one path at the same time that another arrives via the alternative path. This is very confusing; but unless the reflected sound coming over the longer path is intensified by focusing from a curved wall, the difficulties arising from this cause are not great. Architects, however, have so frequently made a practice of putting arched domes and curved recesses into our buildings that many bad echoes haunt our auditoriums to-day. Once the fault is built in, it is usually a matter of considerable difficulty and expense to obtain even a partial cure. A complete cure is usually out of the question. With the exercise of a little intelligence it is possible for the architects to have their curves and the audience to enjoy their concerts as well.

The reflecting qualities of the walls may be determined by means of calculation and models long before the building is constructed. Yet architects do not seem to be completely disgraced if they neglect such precautions. At least not at present, altho the time is rapidly approaching when an acoustical error will be considered as inexcusable as a structural one.

Sounds We Cannot Hear

Whether or not there can be sounds that one cannot hear is perhaps a question for the psychologists to consider. That there are waves exactly like those which produce the sensation of sound in our ears, but of a frequency of vibration far beyond the audible, is well known. If not being able to detect them with our ears means that they cannot rightly be called sound, then one can refer to their study as ultrasonics, as is often done. This study began with the sinking of the Titanic. It was suggested that these short waves be used to determine the location of rocks, icebergs, derelicts, etc. At that time a complete method was suggested and worked out by the English scientist, Lewis Richardson; but nothing practical came out of it. We lacked sufficiently powerful means, at that time, for producing the ultrasonic waves. Such means, however, have recently become available with the radio. The soundless waves can be produced by electrostatic transmitters, by electrodynamic oscillators, or by the use of piezo-electric crystals. These crystals have the unusual property of changing their dimensions whenever a voltage is placed across them. By the use of an oscillator, similar to that used in broadcasting, the voltage across such a crystal can be changed as much as 100,000 or even 500,000 times a second. By expanding and contracting, in synchronism with these changes, the crystal produces the ultrasonic vibrations. This method is the one most generally used.

When beams of these short waves are projected to the bottom of the ocean they return almost as if the ocean bottom were a perfect reflector. Since their speed under water is known, the length of time for them to reach the bottom and return gives us a measure of the distance traveled. Hence the depth of the water is measured. One may well ask how these waves are detected on return, since they cannot be heard. It is done by heterodyning. In this method one produces a second sound which is almost of the same frequency as the first. If both enter the ear at the same time, one hears a sound which has a frequency equal to the difference between the two original frequencies. In this way they are rendered detectable by the ear alone. Such waves in the sonic depth-finder render useful service daily. This method of depth-finding has a great advantage over the usual lead plummet in that it can be employed continuously while a vessel is in motion. It will also detect the presence of icebergs, submarines, and so on. More recent devices give a constant visible record.

Ultrasonic waves can also be used for underwater signaling by the dot-dash system, or the voice may be impressed on these waves much as it is impressed on broadcast-carrier waves. Thus these waves may be employed as carriers for an underwater telephone system.

A peculiar property of these waves is their ability to kill fish and small undersea life. Just why they are capable of doing this is not as yet well understood, but the general opinion among biologists is that the waves disrupt the cells. As these waves have been described as very rapid and slight squeezes and tensions in the propagating body, this theory seems tenable. Such waves will also cause explosive materials to explode, and as such materials are exploded by compressions, it would appear that this view is further justified.

Ultrasonic waves might be of considerable service in the field of chemistry. They have great ability to fractionate materials and produce emulsions. In this way emulsions of mercury and of oil in water have been made. Their ability in this direction is so great that they will even split off particles of glass from the sides of a vessel containing water under which the waves are produced. Small particles of glass will be found floating about in the water.

If a tapered needle-like glass rod has its end dipped in a vessel of oil in which supersonic waves exist, the oil will climb up the rod and be given off its end as a mist. If one touches the end of the rod with the finger the finger will be burned.

An ultrasonic beam can be used under water as a guide to ships. Any vessel suitably equipped can pick up the beam and follow it safely past obstacles. It also enables vessels to communicate with shore or with other ships. It is limited in its use to straight channels, however. It is interesting to note that frequent trouble is encountered near shore from the supersonic waves produced by the rubbing together of pebbles. Computation shows that they should be expected to produce these sounds. Another noisy member of the ocean's bottom is the hitherto unsuspected clam. It is found that from the supersonic viewpoint he is a very noisy animal indeed. He constitutes a nuisance in ultrasonic measurements near shore.

X

THE CONQUEST OF THE AIR

Metal Planes, All Wings and Tail

In spite of all the advance that has been made in the last few years, airplanes to-day look very much as they did several years ago. They are not very different from the planes which the Wrights flew at Kitty Hawk more than a quarter of a century ago. True, the streamline effect, the cross-section of the wings, and all that, have been changed. These are improvements on the original model, not deviations from it.

Airplanes have crossed the Atlantic in both directions, they have stayed in the air for weeks at a time, they have attained speeds of over three hundred miles an hour, they have carried as many as 169 passengers at a single load, they have been powered with engines sufficiently strong to drive them straight up from the ground, and yet the fundamental principles of airplane design have not varied. They have merely been improved upon. The Belgian scientist, Maurice Boel, who has made an exhaustive study of the flights of birds, is of the opinion that his study can add nothing more than a few suggestions to the knowledge of airplane construction. Nothing revolutionary has come out of his studies, they have merely pointed the way which minor changes must take. We have excelled the bird in almost every branch of flight. We still have something to gain in efficiency, but that is about all.

Perhaps the greatest change in the appearance of the planes has been brought about by the introduction of the all-metal plane. In the early days of flying an all-metal plane would have been considered a madman's dream; not only because of the weight, but also because of the corrosion, which in itself would be enough—it would have been thought at that time—to make such a project ridiculous. Those better acquainted with the behavior of metals would also have thought of crystallization and the resultant cracking due to the vibration. There were many reasons why metal could not be used and apparently none in its favor. But we have the all-metal plane, and it promises to be the plane of the future. This is because of the introduction of new corrosion resisting, vibration-resisting, lighter-than-aluminum metals, the latest thing in alloys. The introduction of metal has greatly simplified design. It means less bracing.

Simplicity of appearance is also being accomplished by drawing the engines into the wings. This cuts down the wing resistance and adds greatly to the efficiency. Our largest multimotored planes are all being built in this fashion to-day. There is even a tendency to get rid of the fusilage entirely and to produce planes that are all wings and tail. At least one large passenger plane, now under construction, is being built in this way. The fusilage is wing-shaped and adds its share to the lifting power of the plane. The passengers will be, in reality, inside a wing.

Another change in design is the introduction of the so-called slotted wing. The slot is a safety device intended to give the plane greater stability, and it has proved of great value. The drawback to this device is that, as might be expected, it takes some of the control out of the hands of the pilot. The experienced pilot does not like this; he prefers to rely on his own ability to handle the plane. Thus the introduction of the slotted wing has been somewhat hampered.

Speeding Up the Take-Off

The major problem confronting the designers of airplanes to-day is that of reducing the space necessary for taking off and landing. For transport planes, heavily loaded, even our best air ports to-day are none too large, and in the case of a forced landing it is next to impossible to find a space which will accommodate these machines. To reduce this space a quicker take-off and a lowered landing speed are needed.

The introduction of wheel brakes has helped

a great deal in both these directions. In the past designers have relied upon the tail-skid to bring their planes to a stop. This skid dragged on the ground at the take-off and prevented a rapid rise. The introduction of wheel brakes made it possible to hold the plane stationary until the engine was up to full speed. The brakes also made it possible to replace the skid with a wheel and so to cut down the space necessary for a take-off. This was obviously a great advantage.

Another step in the direction of quicker take-off and lower landing speeds has been the introduction of the so called autogyroplane. This has a four-bladed fan of large dimensions mounted on a vertical shaft above the plane. The lift of the blades helps get the plane off the ground more quickly and enables it to come to rest at very slow speeds and consequently in a short distance. Such a plane remained stationary over Paris for a period of twenty minutes during tests. It is also true that the rotation of the windmill, as it is sometimes called, adds greatly to the stability of the plane. It is claimed that the stability is so great that it can be safely operated by a wholly inexperienced person.

Tests on the autogyro have shown that its efficiency is somewhat less than that of the average plane in use to-day. This has militated against its general acceptance. It is felt that the advantages can be gained in other ways without the sacrifice of efficiency. One of the schemes which, according to the designers, is now in the experimental stage, is the use of auxiliary vertically-mounted engines which will drive the usual type of propeller during the landing and take-off. This, in effect, would be borrowing from the autogyro its scheme for take-off and landing, but dispensing for the present with the stabilizing effect during flight. This seems like a sensible procedure. It is generally known that little of the danger of flying occurs during the actual flight. Most of the accidents are on the take-off or on the landing, the latter period accounting for most of them.

In order to gain greater speed at the take-off —to shorten the distance needed before rising— the use of rockets is now being tried out. A battery of rockets would give a plane startling acceleration. A set of rockets held in reserve is also suggested for the purpose of clearing obstructions which might suddenly appear when flying through a fog. This idea, which has as yet hardly been tried (a single short flight with rockets has been made), promises to be the next step in the quest for a quick take-off.

Attempts are being made to lighten the landing gear. If this can be done it will become the practice on all planes to pull the landing gear up into the body of the plane during flight. This would, in general, increase the speed on fast planes as much as fifty miles an hour. At the present time most landing gears are too heavy to be pulled up by any simple mechanical means. Shock absorbers are now regularly added to the landing gear for greater comfort on landing.

Airplane Engines

Wind resistance is being cut down in every possible way in the newer planes. One of the most recent innovations to contribute to this end has been the introduction of chemical cooling. A substance much more effective than water for engine-cooling has been developed, which will make it possible not only to reduce greatly the size of airplane radiators, but also to put the engine's cylinders in a straight line. At present, in the case of air-cooling, it is necessary to expose all the cylinders to the direct wind created by the plane in order to get sufficient cooling. It has not been found possible, by any other means, to get enough circulation around the cooling-fins of the cylinders. The same has been true of water-cooled engines. To put the cylinders in line would require a water-circulation over distances which have not been found practical. The new liquid will make cylinders in line possible. This will mean that we can stream-line the engine and so greatly cut down the head resistance here as well as in the reduced radiator size.

THE CONQUEST OF THE AIR

The introduction of the flying Diesel engine marks one of the most interesting and probably the most important advances in engine design in many years. Burning oil instead of gasoline adds to the safety of air travel immeasurably. Not only will it make fire almost a negligible factor while flying, but it will also eliminate the dangers of fire and explosion in the event of a crash. Crashes have snuffed out many lives that might have been saved but for the presence of gasoline. And because of the greater efficiency of the Diesel engine, the same supply of fuel in gallons will give twenty per cent. greater cruising range to the airplane. The ignition system is dispensed with in the Diesel, the ignition taking place in the cylinders, owing to the high temperature of compression. The compression is about eight times that of the gasoline engine. This removes a source of possible engine failure and at the same time eliminates a source of interference with radio signals.

Engines are constantly being made with greater and greater power. Not many years ago 150 to 200 horse-power engines were the rule. To-day they run 400 to 500 horse-power, commonly. Engines of as much as 1,000 horse-power have been used in racing planes, and it is freely predicted that engines of 1,200 horse-power will soon be in use. Even with such large engines, because of the increasing size of the planes, multimotored planes are becoming the rule. The increased safety of the multimotored plane is also a factor which is driving us to this method of propulsion.

One of the most interesting predictions that have recently been made is that in the near future we may expect to see gliders driven by outboard motors. The Bureau of Aeronautics of the United States Department of Commerce is responsible for this prediction. We now have gliders and we also have outboard motors. If someone should put the two together it would not be surprizing. As gliders sell for as low as a hundred dollars, and outboard motors for little more, this would give everyone a chance at aviation. In the past most of our planes have been designed primarily for military purposes. Our commercial planes have been copies of these. This has restricted the design and has also kept the planes much alike in size. Now that commercial aviation is becoming able to stand on its own feet, we may expect to see as much diversity of design here as we see in boats, for example, which range from the canoe up to lake steamers, freighters, and ocean liners. There will be planes for many and various purposes, each with its characteristic design.

In the matter of propulsion, much work is being done in the field of variable-pitch propellers. Changes in operating conditions are reflected in the efficiency of the airplane largely in the propeller pitch. If this can be varied to suit the changing conditions, it will add greatly to the operating efficiency. There is already much reason to believe that this problem has been solved by more than one individual.

Flying Blind

Flying has brought with it a host of new navigation instruments. All the old instruments, used for so many years on ships, have proved almost worthless for navigation of the air. Take the compass, for example. Because of the vibration of the plane, and often because of the lack of anything like an even keel, the magnetic compass is useless. This has led to the introduction of an entirely new instrument, the induction compass, which was made famous by the transatlantic flight of Colonel Lindbergh. This instrument depends, like the magnetic compass, on the earth's magnetic field. Coils of wire turning in the earth's field constitute a current generator. It is in fact a small dynamo using the earth's field as magnetic poles instead of having, as in the usual dynamo, poles built into it. The amount of current generated in this way is made to depend on the direction of the airplane by varying the position of the brushes which collect the current generated. When one has chosen his direction the brushes are set to give zero current, and a variation to one side or the other of this direction will move the brushes so as to give either a positive or a negative value of current. Thus, once the direction has been chosen, one has only to keep the plane headed in such a way as to keep the needle of the instrument on zero to be sure that the direction he chose is being followed. Errors sometimes occur, however, owing to lack of uniformity in the earth's magnetic field.

To guide aviators on their course the radio beacon has recently come much into use. This may be of two types. In one a narrow beam of short-wave-length rays is focused and directed along the path to be followed. As long as the aviator is in this narrow beam he can hear the radio signals, but they are lost if he departs from it. In this way he is kept on the course. The other type uses two radio stations and the aviator is able to determine his position from the angle between these two beams as they reach him. Instruments now available do this for him automatically, so that he knows his course at all times. It requires no calculation on his part.

But knowing his location is not enough. The aviator also must know at times how high he is. This is often difficult or impossible to determine in night-flying or in fogs. For this reason altimeters have been devised. One of these operates by the interference of short radio waves. A wave is sent to the ground, reflected, and combined with the original wave, which is still being sent out. The condition of interference between these two waves, original and reflected, is made evident by a change of intensity of the resultant audible signal. In this way the height above the earth is determined. This method operates best at high altitudes and is of little service in landing in the dark or fog. To meet this need an altimeter has been devised for low altitudes. It depends upon a differential capacity effect between a pair of metal plates on the fuselage and the earth. This device makes it possible to know the height accurately right up to within a few feet of landing. The radio beacon and the altimeter, together with other instruments necessary to flying, make it possible to fly blind. In tests it has been demonstrated that an experienced aviator can take off, fly over considerable distance, return to the original airfield, and land successfully without the aid of sight. We can now fly wholly in the dark.

The aviator can receive weather reports while in flight. While he usually knows before taking off what weather to expect, the conditions sometimes change greatly, even in half an hour. In this event the aviator is warned by interrupting his signal beacon. He then, by remote control, tunes in his radio receiver and gets the message intended for him.

In the last few years tremendous strides have been made in the development of airfield flood-lights and beacons. Lights of beam-candle-power ranging up into the millions are common. It is now generally agreed, however, that our main airways are lighted about as well as we can hope for in the present stage of lighting science. Recently much has been done with neon beacons in the hope of greater fog penetration with the red rays. For equal intensities of red and white light the red would be the more penetrating of the two. But white light can be produced in an arc which will contain as much red in addition to the other colors which go to make up white, as is contained in the ordinary neon lamp. Thus, until the neon lamp can be made much more powerful than it now is, it can offer little advantage in fog penetration.

Metal Ships Lighter than Air

The success of the German airship, the *Graf Zeppelin*, has again turned the attention of the world to this type of transportation. Something of the disrepute into which the airship had fallen has been wiped away, the numerous accidents have been forgotten, and once more we are asking, "What is the future of the lighter-than-air flying machine?"

It is true that the lighter-than-air machine is a practical device in one sense of the word. The

Graf Zeppelin has demonstrated this in its round-the-world flight. And yet not very much improvement has been made in this machine as compared to its predecessors. Perhaps the only notable change has been in the fuel. This ship has adopted blau gas for fuel—a petroleum product which has a density about equal to that of air. Thus, as the gas is used up, the weight of the ship and contents does not vary. This makes it unnecessary to valve off the lifting gas as the fuel is used, as is necessary with heavier-than-air fuel, unless some other provision is made to overcome the decreased weight. In the United States dirigible, the *Los Angeles*, the same purpose is accomplished by condensing the water vapor from the engine exhaust. This compensates for loss of weight due to the use of gas. Where blau gas is not available the *Graf Zeppelin* has successfully used other gases or combinations of gases for its engines.

One of the dangers of the lighter-than-air ship has been in the lifting gas. This has almost invariably been hydrogen, which is very explosive when mixed with air. Only in the United States is there a supply of another and safer gas, helium, which can be successfully used as a substitute. As it does not appear likely that helium will ever be found anywhere in great quantities, the dirigibles may have to depend on hydrogen gas if many of them are built, in which case they would always be faced with the danger of explosion.

Another great drawback in the case of the dirigible is its slow speed. This varies from 50 to 100 miles an hour. Normally one takes to the air to gain time, and it is obvious that, at least in overland flight, nothing could be gained over our usual train service. Over long water distances there is some advantage in time, as has been demonstrated by the *Graf Zeppelin*. This ship was built apparently with the thought that this was the only commercial possibility open to such a craft. It still does not appear to be feasible to establish a regular schedule, however.

Perhaps the most interesting development in lighter-than-air machines, from the purely scientific viewpoint, is the all-metal dirigible. It has been possible to build a ship of all metal that is but slightly heavier than the fabric ships. The metal is called alclad. It is an aluminum alloy which, in practise, is coated with a thin layer of aluminum. The aluminum coating resists corrosion better than the alloy. The new United States Navy ship, the *ZMC-2*, is built of alclad fabricated in sheets 0.0095 of an inch in thickness—about three times as thick as a sheet of newspaper.

The use of this metal makes for simplification of construction. It will stand considerable longitudinal stress and consequently many braces and tie-wires can be eliminated from the usual design. The main frame consists of simple hoops of an aluminum alloy, which are lightened by a cellular construction.

In the past the great advantage of the dirigible has been in the number of passengers it could carry. But now its passenger-carrying record has been equaled by the airplane. It is difficult to see, then, just what the future has in store for the Zeppelin type of airship; but it will doubtless make a place for itself. Man has the satisfaction, at least, of knowing that he can build such machines, that he can conquer the air in more ways than one.

BIBLIOGRAPHY

Julius Stieglitz, editor, *Chemistry in Medicine.*
Maurice Holland, *Industrial Explorers.*
Frederick William Wile, editor, *A Century of Industrial Progress.*
H. H. Sheldon and E. N. Grisewood, *Television.*
Waldemar Kaempffert, editor, *A Popular History of American Invention.*
R. A. Millikan, *The Electron.*
John Mills, *Within the Atom.*
A. S. Eddington, *The Nature of the Physical World; Science and the Unseen World.*
J. H. Jeans, *The Universe Around Us.*
De Kruif, *Microbe Hunters.*
Dorsey, *Why We Behave Like Human Beings.*
Humphreys, *Why the Weather.*
E. E. Free and Francis Hoke, *Weather.*
T. C. Chamberlain, *The Sun's Children.*
William F. Ogburn, editor, *Social Changes in 1928.*
Hugh Farrell, *What Price Progress.*